D1594762

THE DESIGN, SAMPLE HANDLING, AND APPLICATIONS OF INFRARED MICROSCOPES

A symposium sponsored by
ASTM Committee E-13 on
Molecular Spectroscopy and
Federation of Analytical Chemistry
and Spectroscopy Societies (FACSS)
Philadelphia, PA, 30 Sept. 1985

ASTM SPECIAL TECHNICAL PUBLICATION 949
Patricia B. Roush, Perkin-Elmer
Corporation, editor

ASTM Publication Code Number (PCN)
04-949000-39

 1916 Race Street, Philadelphia, PA 19103

Library of Congress Cataloging-in-Publication Data

The Design, sample handling, and applications of
infrared microscopes.

(ASTM Special technical publication; 949)
"ASTM publication code number (PCN) 04-949000-39."
Includes bibliographies and indexes.
1. Infrared spectroscopy—Congresses. 2. Fourier
transform spectroscopy—Congresses. 3. Microscope and
microscopy—Congresses. I. Roush, Patricia B.
II. ASTM Committee E-13 on Molecular Spectroscopy.
III. Federation of Analytical Chemistry and Spectroscopy
Societies. IV. Infrared microscopes. V. Series.
QD96.I5.D47   1987   543'.08583   87-14345
0-8031-0953-9

Printed in Ann Arbor, MI
August 1987

FOREWORD

The symposium on The Design, Sample Handling, and Applications of Infrared Microscopes was held in Philadelphia, Pennsylvania, 30 September 1985. The symposium was sponsored by ASTM Committee E-13 on Molecular Spectroscopy and Federation of Analytical Chemistry and Spectroscopy Societies (FACSS). Patricia B. Roush, Perkin-Elmer Corporation, presided as symposium chairman and editor of this publication.

Related
ASTM Publications

Computerized Quantitative Infrared Analysis, STP 934 (1987), 04-934000-39

Advances in Luminescence Spectroscopy, STP 863 (1985), 04-863000-39

New Directions in Molecular Luminescence, STP 822 (1983), 04-822000-39

Index on Mass Spectral Date, AMD 11 (1969), 10-011000-39

Sampling, Standards, and Homogeneity, STP 540 (1973), 04-540000-34

A Note of Appreciation
to Reviewers

The quality of the papers that appear in this publication reflects not only the obvious efforts of the authors but also the unheralded, though essential, work of the reviewers. On behalf of ASTM we acknowledge with appreciation their dedication to high professional standards and their sacrifice of time and effort.

ASTM Committee on Publications

ASTM Editorial Staff

Helen M. Hoersch
Janet R. Schroeder
Kathleen A. Greene
Bill Benzing

Contents

Overview

In the spring of 1985, when this symposium was first planned, the use of a microscope as an accessory in a Fourier transform infrared (FT-IR) spectrometer was still somewhat a new concept. The symposium was planned as a means of introducing many people to this new technique. The day long symposium, which was part of the 1985 Federation of Analytical Chemistry and Spectroscopy Societies (FACSS) meeting, consisted of papers which covered design considerations, sample handling, and applications to such areas as fibers and polymers.

This volume consists of nine peer-reviewed papers that were presented at that symposium. As such they serve as an introduction to the field of infrared microscopy. The technique is growing very rapidly. ASTM E13.03 on Infrared Spectroscopy has a task group that is working on standards for IR microanalysis that will include sections on FT-IR microscopes. During the fall of 1986 there were two symposia organized on the topic; one at the 1986 FACSS meeting and one at the 1986 Eastern Analytical Symposium (EAS) meeting. The proceedings from both of these symposia are also being written. With the introduction of this STP and the proceedings from the two 1986 symposia, there will be valuable references for a spectroscopist who is getting involved in FT-IR microscope analysis.

The title of this Special Technical Publication, The Design, Sample Handling, and Applications of Infrared Microscopes, was chosen to be descriptive of the material found in this volume. Some of the design criteria for infrared microscopes are discussed by Messerschmidt. Both a custom-built microscope (Katon et al.) and a modification of a commercial instrument (Miseo and Guilmette) are discussed. All of the authors deal with sample handling to some extent in their papers. In particular, however, the papers by Humecki and Shearer et al. describe sample handling and the tools that are needed in great detail. These two papers would be the perfect place for the spectroscopist who is just getting an FT-IR microscope to start. They would provide a shopping list of other necessary tools his FT-IR microscopy laboratory would need. The entire purpose for the FT-IR microscope is to make it possible to analyze very small specimens or very small contaminants in specimens. Because of this, the entire volume deals with applications. There are several papers dealing with fiber analysis (Bartick, Chase, and Katon et al.) and two dealing with polymer analysis (Harthcock and Mirabella).

In "Photometric Considerations in the Design and Use of Infrared Microscope Accessories" Messerschmidt discusses some of the problems associated with FT-IR microscopy and how to prevent them. The major limitation for successful application of FT-IR microscopy is related to the diffraction theorem. This theorem is explained in detail as it applies to the infrared region and to the use of the FT-IR microscopes. By understanding the diffraction theorem, the spectroscopist is able to deal better with the limitations it imposes on the analysis. Two techniques are presented to deal with the problems caused by diffraction. These are ultramicroscopy and redundant aperturing. Both of these techniques were very new to FT-IR microscopy when this symposium was presented in the fall of 1985. Since that time a commercially available FT-IR microscope, the IR-Plan from Spectra-Tech, has been introduced which allows for redundant aperturing.

"FT-IR Microspectrophotometry as a Failure Analysis Tool" by Shearer and Peters mainly describes sample handling and the tools needed for FT-IR microscopy. This chapter is an excellent one for the analyst new to FT-IR microscopy. It describes some of the basic features of FT-IR microscopes as well as the basic sampling tools that the FT-IR microscopist would need.

The chapter by Humecki presents the spectroscopist with sampling information that optical microscopists have been using for many years. He also describes how to make what he calls a capillary brush. The capillary brush allows you to pyrolyze a specimen that is less than one microgram in size. A particle is pushed into the capillary brush and the end sealed in a microflame. The specimen is pyrolyzed by heating the capillary brush. The end of the brush is then broken off and a tiny amount of solvent is added. The solvent and specimen are dripped onto a salt plate, the solvent evaporated, and the pyrolyzate can be analyzed. This is just one example of the many useful techniques that are described. The IR spectroscopist who is dealing with FT-IR microscopes can learn a great deal about handling small samples from the optical microscopist.

Chase discusses some of the limitations of FT-IR microscopy and how the problems can be overcome. He describes some of the problems that Messerschmidt discussed in an earlier chapter. Once again the need for physical masking at the specimen, rather than a simple aperture at an image plane, is stressed. This appears to be essential for any quantitative work with the microscope accessory. One of the advantages of the FT-IR microscope that is pointed up in the paper is the ability to look at single fibers. By first characterizing the polarization characteristics of the FT-IR and the microscope, it is possible to measure a dichroic spectrum on a single fiber.

In "Considerations for Fiber Sampling With Infrared Microspectroscopy" Bartick deals with the specimen handling issues for fibers. Three different size categories are described, and the way each different diameter fiber is best prepared and handled is discussed. Techniques for flattening fibers to reduce the thickness of the fiber and therefore reduce the tendency for it to act as a lens are described. An important point about spectral subtractions is that all of the parameters must be the same. For FT-IR microspectroscopic analysis this means that the same specimen technique and aperture size must be used in order to obtain valid results.

Katon et al. also describe techniques for fiber analysis. The problem of the beam being defocused due to the cylindrical shape of the fiber is discussed. Several ways to prevent this include flattening the fiber prior to analysis or measuring the fiber in a diamond anvil cell. At the time of the symposium not much work was being done with diamond anvil cells in FT-IR microscopes. Most likely this was due to the fact that the diamond anvil cell did not fit into many of the commercial microscopes. Katon et al. describe a custom-built microscope and the results they obtained with the diamond anvil cell. Since the symposium more commercial FT-IR microscopes can accommodate diamond anvil cells, and this will certainly be a field of further growth.

The paper by Miseo and Guilmette describes using the FT-IR microscope for several very difficult kinds of industrial problems. One of these dealt with identifying an additive in ink. They cast a spot of ink onto a silver chloride plate and in effect performed a chromatographic separation of the ink using methylene chloride. After separating the original spot into several smaller spots, those spots were further separated with methylene chloride. The various spots on the silver chloride plate were analyzed using the FT-IR microscope. This paper may well describe the first use of the FT-IR microscope for TLC type analysis. Since this symposium was held, the use of FT-IR microscopes for analyzing chromatographic fractions has become very popular and will most likely continue to be.

Harthcock describes some of the advantages of FT-IR microscopy over traditional infrared microsampling techniques. The applications in this chapter and the next chapter by Mirabella deal with polymer analysis. The use of FT-IR microscopes in the analysis of contaminants in polymers is a growing technique. One of the applications that Harthcock describes is the study of multilayer polymer films. A cross section of the polymer laminate is first obtained by microtoming it to the appropriate thickness. The various layers of the laminate can be then analyzed using FT-IR microscopy. By masking the specimen, layers as thin as 10 to 15 μm can be measured. One problem is that spectra cannot be readily obtained from layers that are thinner than 10 μm by using the FT-IR microscope. However, attenuated total reflectance (ATR) can be used as a complementary technique to study these specimens. By using both techniques Harthcock was able to analyze the laminate more completely.

Mirabella's paper describes two applications using the FT-IR microscope to analyze polymers. One of these involves the analysis of a multilayer film by using a combination of FT-IR microscopy and ATR. Being able to identify successfully the individual layers of a multilayer specimen is of critical importance to the polymer industry. This application may well become one of the most popular industrial uses of the FT-IR microscope. The other application that Mirabella describes is a novel technique involving the simultaneous measurement of thermal property response and infrared spectra using a differential scanning calorimeter (DSC) and an FT-IR microscope. The DSC microscopy cell was used with sodium chloride windows, rather than the standard sapphire windows used for optical microscopy. The DSC microscopy cell was then placed in the FT-IR microscope. This allowed for simultaneous measurement of FT-IR spectra before, during, and after the melting of the polymer specimen. Using this combined technique it may be possible to correlate the thermally induced changes in the infrared spectra with the effects on particular chemical bonds.

In my overview of this STP I have tried to cover briefly some of the highlights of the individual papers. One paper that is sadly absent from the volume is the one presented by Tomas Hirschfeld at the symposium in 1985. His untimely death in April 1986 occurred before his paper was completed. We will all certainly miss Tomas, his friendship, and his enormous contributions to so many areas of spectroscopy. Because of this, I would like to dedicate this STP to the memory of Tomas B. Hirschfeld.

Patricia B. Roush

Perkin-Elmer Corporation, Norwalk, CT 06859-0903; symposium chairman and editor.

D. Bruce Chase[1]

Infrared Microscopy: A Single-Fiber Technique

REFERENCE: Chase, D. B., **"Infrared Microscopy: A Single-Fiber Technique,"** *The Design, Sample Handling, and Applications of Infrared Microscopes, ASTM STP 949*, P. B. Roush, Ed., American Society for Testing and Materials, Philadelphia, 1987, pp. 4–11.

ABSTRACT: The advantages and limitations of Fourier transform infrared spectrophotometry (FT-IR) microscopy are discussed. Use of a single aperture at an image plane leads to drastic reductions in photometric accuracy in the spectra of single fibers. Improved performance can be achieved by using physical aperturing. The polarization properties of the microscope have been determined and infrared dichroic spectra of single fibers are shown.

KEY WORDS: infrared microscopy, dichroic measurements, single-fiber spectroscopy

The successful introduction of microscopes as accessories to infrared interferometers has opened up whole new fields to the industrial spectroscopist. The ability to examine small specimens or regions of specimens and provide qualitative information on their structure can be tremendously helpful in film defect analysis, fiber spectroscopy, and other forms of microanalysis. This capability has generated enthusiastic use of the infrared technique and, unfortunately, some of the problems encountered in infrared microscopy tend to be overlooked.

The lack of good reproduction of the 0 and 100% lines in the transmission spectra obtained on small specimens (<30 μm in diameter) causes a great deal of difficulty in quantitative spectroscopy. Any attempt to extend the study of fibers to include accurate dichroic spectroscopy is bound to fail if the photometric accuracy of the individual polarized spectra is poor. In this study the degradation in photometric accuracy is examined by comparing spectra obtained with image aperturing versus spectra obtained with physical aperturing at the specimen. In addition, the polarization purity is investigated and dichroic ratios are compared with those found using a non-microscopic instrument.

Experimental

A Digilab infrared microscope, equipped with a rectangular aperture and a narrowband MCT detector, was interfaced to a Nicolet 20DX interferometer. All spectra were obtained at nominal 4 cm^{-1} resolution. Five hundred and twelve scans were co-added, and the interferograms were transferred to a VAX 11/750 computer for further processing. A Norton-Beer [1] weak apodization function F3 was used in the Fourier transformation.

An Oriel variable-width monochrometer slit was used to physically mask the fiber specimens. The polarization studies were done with Harrick Scientific wire grid polarizers (KRS-5 substrates, 2048 lines/mm).

---

[1] Research chemist, Central Research and Development Department, E. I. du Pont de Nemours & Co., Wilmington, DE 19898.

The reticle in the microscope was calibrated for size measurements with two Ronchi gratings (100 and 20 lines/mm).

Discussion

As other workers have shown [2], perfectly acceptable, qualitative spectra can be obtained with the infrared microscopes on specimens down to 10 μm in size. The spectra are, however, inevitably plotted with scale expansion. This gives the reader the impression of good reproduction of absorption intensities. A closer examination of the abscissa values will often show otherwise. The first indication of problems associated with stray light and light loss can be seen by examining the transmission of the microscope through the slit at the image plane relative to the full throughput with the slit wide open. Figure 1 shows such a spectrum obtained with a slit measuring 10 by 250 μm (relative to the open beam). One would expect a transmission of approximately 3% through such a slit. The loss in transmission to higher wavelength is undoubtedly due to diffraction and is commonly observed. The average value of the transmission is, however, a factor of three smaller than one would expect assuming homogeneous illumination of the slit. Clearly, intensity is lost through diffraction effects.

These problems may be relatively unimportant so long as the specimen is much larger than the slit being employed. Under these conditions, photons which strike the detector will have had to pass through the specimen. The 100% transmittance (T) line may be perturbed, but the 0%T figure should be relatively unaffected. Figure 2 shows the spectrum of a polysulfone fiber encased in an epoxy matrix. The specimen had been microtomed to provide a thin section, but the resulting flake was quite large (100 μm in diameter). The fiber was approximately 25 μm in diameter. By moving the specimen to one side, a reference spectrum

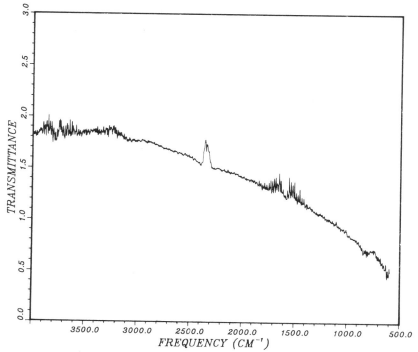

FIG. 1—*Transmission curve for a 10-by-250 μm slit.*

of the epoxy matrix was obtained. Figure 3 shows the subtraction results (presented in transmittance). Compensation of the strong epoxy bands was fairly good, and the characteristic vibrational spectrum of the polysulfone is identifiable. This subtraction succeeds only because the specimen which contributes the strong absorption bands (low transmittance) is large compared with the slit.

When a small specimen is examined, much less reliable results are obtained. A polyethylene terephthalate (PET) fiber approximately 20 μm in diameter gave the spectrum shown in Fig. 4. Clearly the absorption intensities are distorted. The band at 1720 cm^{-1} should have a transmittance of less than 5% as determined by examining the spectrum of a PET film of comparable thickness. Through diffraction effects, light is striking the detector never having passed through the specimen, even though the slit was closed down to 70% of the fiber diameter. In addition, the transmission in nonabsorbing regions (100% line) seems to be lower than one would expect. This effect could well be due to specimen-induced defocusing. In regions of low absorption, the fiber acts as a lens with a relatively high radius of curvature. This serves to defocus the beam, overfilling the detector, and dropping the observed value of 100%T. This problem can certainly be minimized by pressing the specimen before examination to produce a closer approximation to plane parallel faces. This also makes the specimen larger, reducing the problems associated with diffraction.

When the same PET fiber is examined with physical aperturing at the specimen, the spectrum shown in Fig. 5 is obtained. The absorption intensities are now much closer to those expected from a fiber of this thickness. This result would tend to confirm that the problems with the reproduction of the 0%T line are associated with diffraction effects. Rays from outside the sample (Airy disk lobes) are physically blocked from reaching the detector. If relatively accurate photometric values are needed, one must put up with the additional specimen preparation involved in physically masking the specimen.

Before attempting polarization studies on fibers, it was necessary to characterize the polarization characteristics of the optical train in the microscope. If the optics scrambled polarization by themselves, then any dichroic spectra would contain false intensity values. Figure 6 shows transmission curves obtained with two polarizers in the system, one located at the sample point and the second located at the image plane where the variable aperture is normally placed. The two curves were obtained with the polarizers parallel and perpendicular to each other. In the crossed state, extinction is found to be better than 0.05. While this is not as good as obtained in larger systems, it is suitable for our work. The loss in polarization purity may be due to some scrabbling by the low f-number off-axis ellipsoid used to focus the beam onto the specimen.

A further check on the validity of polarized intensities was made by examining an oriented thick film specimen of poly p-phenylene terephthalimide using both the microscope and Nicolet 7199 interferometer equipped with the same polarizers. The dichroic spectrum in a spectral region where the film is not strongly absorbing, obtained on the 7199 is shown in Fig. 7. The spectrum obtained on the microscope is shown in Fig. 8. The agreement is quite good, even to the absolute values of the dichroic ratios.

Figure 9 shows the dichroic spectrum obtained on a single fiber of poly p-phenylene terephthalimide which is known from X-ray studies to be oriented. The spectrum shows the N-H stretching band at 3400 cm^{-1} to be polarized perpendicular to the fiber axis. The use of physical masking at the specimen allowed more accurate polarization intensities to be recorded.

Conclusions

The infrared microscope is an excellent tool for obtaining qualitative data on small spec

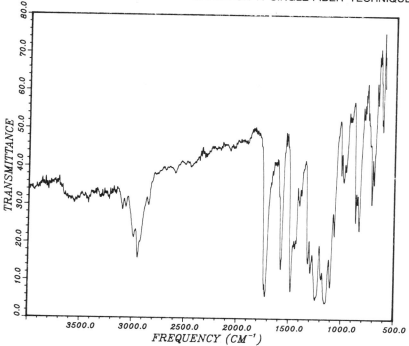

FIG. 2—*Spectrum of polysulfone fiber in an epoxy matrix.*

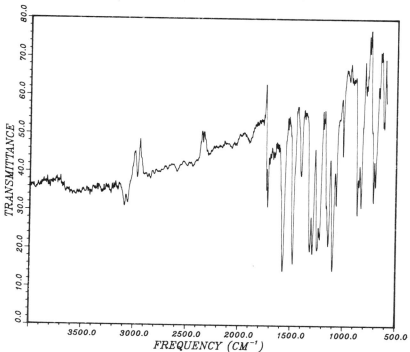

FIG. 3—*Subtraction spectrum polysulfone fiber minus epoxy background.*

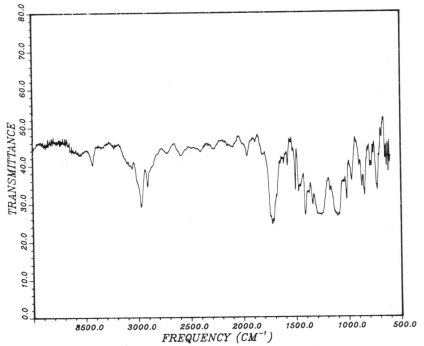

FIG. 4—*Spectrum of single fiber of PET 20 μm in diameter.*

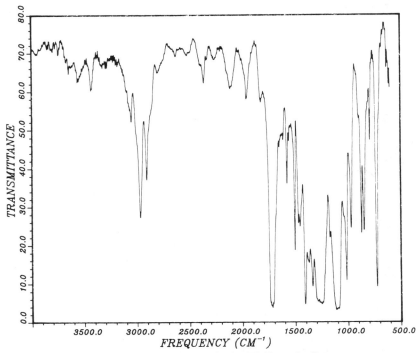

FIG. 5—*Spectrum of single fiber of PET 20 μm in diameter.*

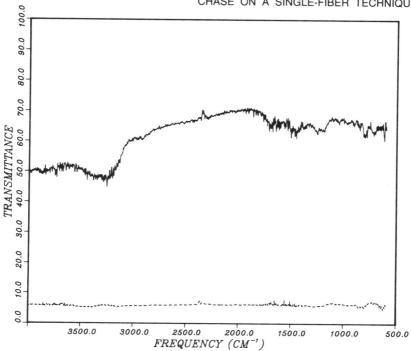

FIG. 6—*Parallel and crossed polarizer spectra through microscope.*

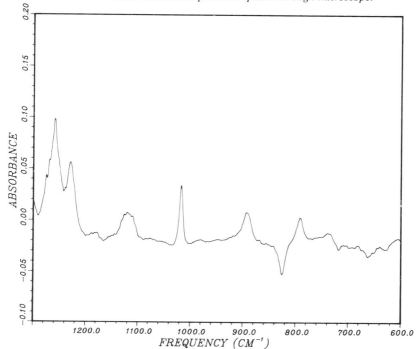

FIG. 7—*Dichroic spectrum poly* p-*phenylene terephthalimide film obtained on 7199 interferometer.*

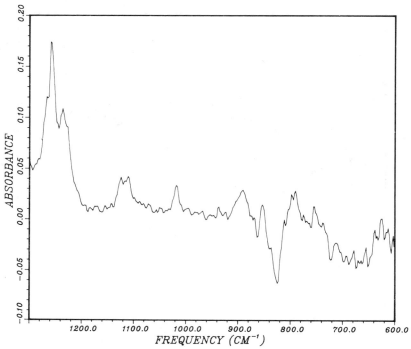

FIG. 8—*Dichroic spectrum poly* p-*phenylene terephthalimide film obtained on microscope.*

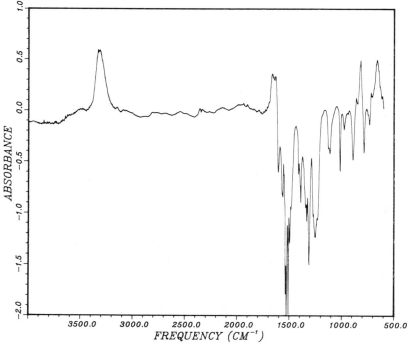

FIG. 9—*Dichroic spectrum poly* p-*phenylene terephthalimide single fiber.*

imens or regions within a specimen. If quantitative data are required, one must avoid the use of a single aperture at the image plane and instead physically mask the specimen. This additional specimen preparation is required to minimize diffraction and stray light effects. The polarization purity of the instrument is acceptable and valid dichroic spectra can be obtained on single fibers.

References

[1] Norton, R. H. and Beer, R. J., *Journal of the Optical Society of America,* Vol. 66, 1976, p. 259.
[2] Krishnan, K., *Polymer Preprints,* Vol. 25 No. 2, 1984, p. 1182.

Robert G. Messerschmidt[1]

Photometric Considerations in the Design and Use of Infrared Microscope Accessories

REFERENCE: Messerschmidt, R. G., **"Photometric Considerations in the Design and Use of Infrared Microscope Accessories,"** *The Design, Sample Handling, and Applications of Infrared Microscopes, ASTM STP 949,* P. B. Roush, Ed., American Society for Testing and Materials, Philadelphia, 1987, pp. 12–26.

ABSTRACT: The field of infrared microspectrometry has become, over the past three years, an important analytical technique, used in conjunction with Fourier transform infrared spectrophotometry (FT-IR). The theoretical limitations of the technique have not before been published. Proper application of the theory can have a significant impact on the attainment of optimal performance from infrared microscope systems. The major limiting issue for the successful application of this technique is the diffraction theorem. This theorem as manifested in the infrared region is explained in detail in this paper, insofar as it is relevant to infrared microsampling.

Several other issues pertinent to the design and use of infrared microspectrometers are also discussed. Specifically, the choice of on-axis mirrors as opposed to lenses or off-axis mirrors in the critical areas of the instrument is explained. Also, specimen-based optical effects are identified and discussed.

Finally, two schemes to deal with the adverse effects of diffraction are presented—ultramicroscopy and redundant aperturing. These have the effect of improving the spatial resolution of the instrument. A spectrum obtained from a 5-μm spot of a polystyrene film is included to demonstrate this improvement.

KEY WORDS: microscopy, spectroscopy, infrared, microsampling, optical theory/diffraction

A recent editorial in *Nature* magazine, in reporting on a new advance in visible light microscopy stated, "The problem with light microscopy is light . . . . The wavelength of light fundamentally limits how well a microscope can resolve two closely spaced point objects." This is very true and has been known for a long time. This fact limits the resolution with a light microscope to about ½ μm. These numbers come from the diffraction equations, which I will go into later on in this paper. In fact, this is the reason that electron microscopes are needed, because of the need to analyze things below the diffraction limit of visible light microscopy.

Diffraction

It is very easy to show that the same resolution laws which are true in the visible region also apply in the infrared region. What makes *our* life worse is that the wavelengths of infrared radiation are 10 to 100 times longer than in the visible, which means that the diffraction limit is 10 to 100 time worse! Accordingly, if two point objects are closer than about 50-μm, they are not resolved over the full mid-infrared. If we can't resolve two

[1] Technical director, Spectra-Tech, Inc., 652 Glenbrook Rd., Stamford, CT 06906.

neighboring point objects, then we can't measure the response from one without seeing some energy impurity from the other. Many people who work with infrared microscope systems have empirically observed this effect. Far and away, diffraction is the biggest reason performance problems and quantitative anomalies are observed in infrared microscope systems.

Figure 1 graphically demonstrates our concern for diffraction imagery. This is a diffraction pattern, or an Airy disk, of the energy emanating from a point source, which is imaged by some optical system to the origin of the graph. It can be seen that the energy from a point, imaged by an optical system does not image ideally to a point, but rather to a central bright spot followed by a succession of dark and bright rings. This is due to the fact that only a portion of the original spherical wavefront can be collected by any real optical system. Some information from the original image is lost, and therefore the image quality is degraded. The bright rings are called lobes or pods, and they contain energy from the original point. It turns out that for any unobscured optical imaging system, there is roughly 85% of the energy in what is called the central maximum of the pattern. The first dark ring would occur

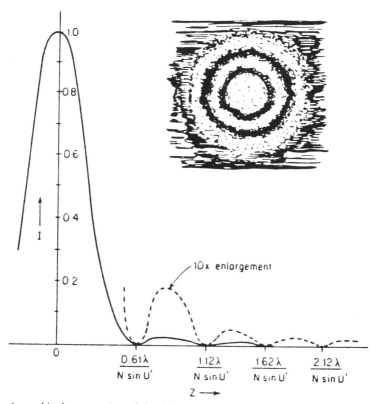

FIG. 1—*A graphic demonstration of the diffraction effect, the Airy disk. A point imaged by an optical system does not image to the same small dimensions as it started out. Energy spreads out into a central bright spot, followed by a series of dark and light rings. Each of the bright rings contains some of the energy from the original spot. With a typical infrared microscope configuration, the first dark ring occurs at 24 μm out from the origin. The fourth dark ring is a 84 μm, and there is still 5% of the energy beyond that, (from Ref 1).*

at 0.61 times the wavelength divided by (n sin u') where u' is the angle of the most extreme ray of the optical system. In this case, the case of the infrared microscope, (n sin u') is the numerical aperture (NA) of the objective being used in the measurement. The numerical aperture, which is simply the "speed" or collection ability of an optical element, is typically somewhere on the order of 0.5, which means that a 60-deg cone of light is collected off the specimen. This is a fairly typical value for infrared microscope objectives.

To try to quantitate what the implications of the resolution limit are for infrared microspectrometry, we should take the longest wavelength that we might be interested in looking at in the infrared—let us say 20 μm (500 wavenumbers). If we plug this into the diffraction equation, along with a numerical aperture of 0.5, we find that the first dark ring occurs at 24 μm out from the specimen. The second dark ring occurs at 44 μm, the third one at 64 and the fourth one at 84 μm. Even after the fourth dark ring, there is still roughly 5% of the energy from a point source outside of that. Obviously this is something to be well aware of in doing infrared microsampling. Table 1 further explains the diffraction effect, for both an infinitely small point source, and an infinitely thin slit source. Figure 2 graphically demonstrates the energy distribution in three dimensions, for both the point and slit cases. Note here that the pods are left off the sketches for clarity. Note also that the slit source diffraction function is simply the point source function's cross section, summed along its length, as we would expect.

In the visible region, very early on researchers tried to quantitate what the diffraction pattern meant to them with regard to whether they could discern two points that were spaced a certain distance apart; Fig. 3 demonstrates this. Clearly, if two points are spaced very closely as in Fig. 3a, where the separation between the maxima of the two points is less

TABLE 1—*A further description of the equations and implications of the diffraction phenomenon. Values are given for the circular and slit-shaped objects (from Ref 3).*

| Ring (or Band) | Circular Aperture | | | Slit Aperture | |
	Z	Peak Illumination	Energy in Ring, %	Z	Peak Illumination
Central maximum	0	1.0	83.9	0	1.0
First dark ring	$\dfrac{0.61\lambda}{N' \sin U'}$	0.0	···	$\dfrac{0.5\lambda}{N' \sin U'}$	0.0
First bright ring	$\dfrac{0.82\lambda}{N' \sin U'}$	0.017	7.1	$\dfrac{0.72\lambda}{N' \sin U'}$	0.047
Second dark ring	$\dfrac{1.12\lambda}{N' \sin U'}$	0.0	···	$\dfrac{1.0\lambda}{N' \sin U'}$	0.0
Second bright ring	$\dfrac{1.33\lambda}{N' \sin U'}$	0.0041	2.8	$\dfrac{1.23\lambda}{N' \sin U'}$	0.017
Third dark ring	$\dfrac{1.62\lambda}{N' \sin U'}$	0.0	···	$\dfrac{1.5\lambda}{N' \sin U'}$	0.0
Third bright ring	$\dfrac{1.85\lambda}{N' \sin U'}$	0.0016	1.5	$\dfrac{1.74\lambda}{N' \sin U'}$	0.0083
Fourth dark ring	$\dfrac{2.12\lambda}{N' \sin U'}$	0.0	···	$\dfrac{2.0\lambda}{N' \sin U'}$	0.0
Fourth bright ring	$\dfrac{2.36\lambda}{N' \sin U'}$	0.00078	1.0	$\dfrac{2.24\lambda}{N' \sin U'}$	0.0050
Fifth dark ring	$\dfrac{2.62\lambda}{N' \sin U'}$	0.0	···	$\dfrac{2.5\lambda}{N' \sin U'}$	0.0

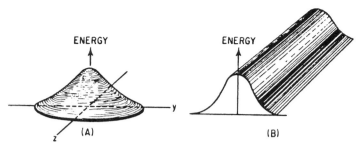

FIG. 2—*Three-dimensional view of the Airy disk, for both circular and slit-shaped objects. The lobes are left off for clarity. Note that the slit source diffraction function is simply the point source function's cross section, summed along the long dimension of the slit (from Ref 1).*

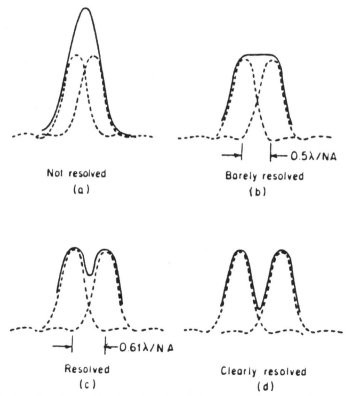

FIG. 3—*Result of the combination of two diffraction patterns close to each other. The solid lines are the envelopes of the energy from each point. The two points are of equal intensity. In (a), the two objects are so close that we could not tell that in fact there were two points instead of one. (b) The barely resolved case, also called the Sparrow criterion for resolution. (c) The resolved case, or the Rayleigh criterion for two points to be just resolved. Beyond this, two points are considered clearly resolved for visual observation, (d). It should be noted that while the Rayleigh or even the Sparrow condition may be good enough for visual observation, we need to be more rigorous for spectral characterization (from Ref 1).*

TABLE 2—*Values of various parameters related to the Airy disk (from Ref 2).*

Ring	Radius of Ring, Z	Relative Intensity	Amount of Light in Ring, %	Light Remaining Outside Ring, %
Center	0.0	1.0	83.9	...
First dark	3.832	...	...	16.1
First bright	5.136	0.0175	7.1	...
Second dark	7.016	...	...	9.0
Second bright	8.417	0.0042	2.8	...
Third dark	10.173	...	...	6.2
Third bright	11.620	0.0016	1.5	...
Fourth dark	13.324	...	...	4.7

than $(0.5\lambda/NA)$, the two points are not resolved. The summation of the two diffraction functions yields a smooth envelope with one maximum. In looking at these points, one would see a blur which would look like one point. Figure 3*b* describes the next case, where the separation between maxima is $(0.5\lambda/NA)$. This is the barely resolved case. This is called the Sparrow criterion for resolution, and these two points would be barely resolvable. Using astronomical telescopes, Sparrow noticed that if two stars were separated by this amount, then he could tell clearly that there were in fact two stars and not just one.

Lord Rayleigh had a slightly more stringent requirement for resolution. His criterion is that two points must be separated by $(0.61\lambda/NA)$. Figure 3*c* shows that the Rayleigh criterion requires a larger separation than the Sparrow criterion. Figure 3*d* shows two points separated even further, resulting in baseline resolution. This is the clearly resolved case. The problem with these criteria for spectroscopy is that all these conditions are concerned only with resolving the central bright ring. This is a perfectly fine situation for visual observation, since the central maximum is 85% of the energy, and our eyes are sensitive to a range of only an order of magnitude of intensity anyway. But a spectrophotometer can deal with a larger range of intensity. We routinely look for analytes absorbing at only 0.001 absorbance units (au). Compared to something absorbing at 1 au, which is sort of a photometric upper

FIG. 4—*Perfect image of an extended object with no diffraction. Assume this object is small enough that we are looking at it under a microscope. Also assume that it is homogeneous, and that it is surrounded only by air.*

limit, there is a difference of three orders of magnitude. In addition, spectral features we are trying to mask out may be more intense than the ones in which we are interested. For photometric answers with a microscope, as opposed to visual answers, we have to also consider the lobes.

Table 2 more clearly describes why we must be aware of energy outside the central maximum. It shows that outside of the fourth dark ring, which we showed earlier to be at four times the wavelength from the origin, there still exists roughly 5% of the energy from the point source. If we look at this in another way, it is perhaps more enlightening. Every point in the field of view of the microscope, when imaged, spreads out into a diffraction pattern. Consider a specimen that is homogeneous and sitting in the microscope field of view, with nothing surrounding it but air. The postage stamp of Fig. 4 demonstrates this case. Now consider two neighboring points in the field, one on the specimen, and one in air, right next to the specimen. Since each of these points spreads out into a diffraction pattern, their energies overlap each other. Figure 5 shows that for relatively large specimens, this overlapping causes a dilution/contamination of signal at the edges, and the specimen at the center remains pure, uncontaminated by stray light. But Fig. 6 illustrates that for smaller specimens, the entire specimen is somewhat contaminated by stray light from outside the specimen.

The area at the center of the specimen still has the least impurity. Note that if instead of air surrounding the specimen there are other spectral features, then these features will contaminate our specimen. When the quality of the optical system is not sufficient to discriminate against stray signal from surrounding areas, spectral subtraction can be used, but with the following caveats. First, since diffraction is wavelength dependent, the reference spectrum should be measured at the same field stop (variable aperture) setting as was used for the sample. Otherwise a slope would be apparent, causing bad subtractions. Second, the optical system which is not well corrected has, by definition, a lower energy density. This results in noisier spectra, complicated further by the noise introduced by the subtraction process. Finally, recording two spectra and subtracting is just plainly more time-consuming than measuring one high-quality spectrum. Later on in this paper, two ways of further

FIG. 5—*Diffraction of a microscopic object where the object is quite large (bigger than 100 μm). In this case, energy from the points in space directly outside of the object dilutes the image, but mainly at the edges. Substantial energy in the center of the object remains relatively pure. Simply overaperturing the object can virtually eliminate the problem.*

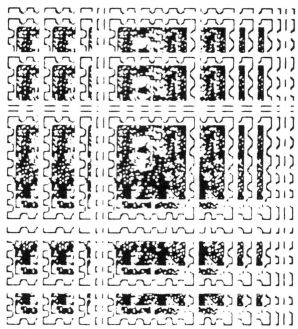

FIG. 6—*Diffracted image of the object where diffraction is of the same order or larger than the object (up to about 50 μm). No parts of the object remain pure, and no amount of overaperturing eliminates the problem, although it does reduce the problem significantly. In this case, there will always be some stray signal from neighboring points in the spectrum, either stray light or spectral features.*

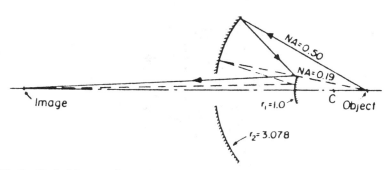

FIG. 7—*Typical layout of an infrared microscope objective, ×10 power, along with its paraxial raytrace. Note that the small "secondary" mirror obscures some of the energy. In addition to the loss of energy, there is an effect on the diffraction pattern for such an optic. Some more of the energy from the central maximum is thrown into the lobes, as is described in the next figure (from Ref 2).*

improving spatial resolution will be shown—redundant aperturing and ultramicroscopy. Without these resolution-enhancement techniques, if our specimen of interest is smaller than about 50-μm there will be a noticeable stray light component in the spectrum.

There is one other complication which comes into play because of the type of optics we must use on an infrared microscope. The diffraction patterns that I showed earlier were for unobstructed imaging systems. In infrared microscopes, we have to use reflective on-axis optics, and these necessarily have a central obscuration. In most objectives the central obscuration is on the order of 10%. The effect of this is to throw some of the energy from the central bright maximum into the lobes or pods. Therefore, diffraction is even a little worse than the numbers shown before. Figure 7 shows a general layout of a Cassegrainian infrared microscope objective. The small mirror (secondary) obstructs energy as it passes to the large mirror (primary). Figure 8 shows the effect on the diffraction pattern for both

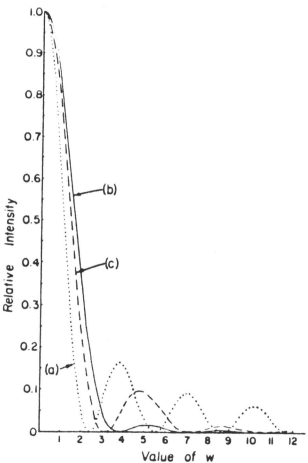

FIG. 8—*Airy disk for a centrally obscured optical system. An unobscured pattern is shown for reference (b), along with a theoretical 100% obscured system (a). The curve (c) shows a 50% obscured system, area-wise. Most infrared microscope objectives are only 10 to 20% obscured (from Ref 2).*

a 50% obscuration and for a theoretical 100% obscuration. The net effect is that the lobes become still more important to our energy calculations.

It should be comforting to know, at least, that the these diffraction effects will not change the wavenumber position or the frequency resolution of the measurement. The issue is solely one of band intensity, both absolute and also relative to other bands in the spectrum.

Nondiffraction-Related Effects

Although diffraction is far and away the biggest enemy of the infrared microspectroscopist, there are some other sampling anomalies to be aware of. The first is that a fiber-shaped specimen can act as a lens. If energy entering the fiber is not focussed exactly at the center of the fiber, then the specimen will de-focus the incoming energy. The effect is to displace the point of zero absorbance between the specimen and background spectra. Another effect encountered with fiber-shaped specimen is the wedge cell effect. Some of the input radiation goes through the specimen in a thin part, while other rays see a thicker part of the specimen, as is clearly shown in Fig. 9. The result is a range of sample pathlengths, causing deviations from Beer's law. If photometrically accurate results are required from a fiber specimen, the best bet is to flatten it out, although this destroys orientation information. There are many good ways of flattening microspecimens. Some of the techniques are borrowed from the light microscopy field. Squeezing the specimen between salt plates, rolling with a polished roller, or pressing with polished anvils are all good ways of flattening specimens. Much less force than expected is needed to flatten many small specimens, due to the small area and resultant large pressure for small forces.

If the specimen has parallel faces, but a refractive index much greater than unity, then it can also cause a beam displacement. Figure 10 illustrates this effect. Quantitatively, the shift is equal to $(n - 1)t/n$, where n is the refractive index of the specimen, and t is its

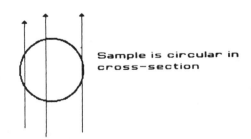

Some rays see longer pathlengths than others. The effect is that of a wedged cell. Good for dynamic range, bad for quantitative analysis and library search.

Sample is circular in cross-section

Transmitted energy

FIG. 9—*A circular-cross-section specimen, shown to demonstrate two photometric anomalies caused by it. First, the specimen is shaped like a very strong lens, and as such it can displace the focus of the beam considerably. Second, since some infrared rays go through a longer pathlength than others, the effect is that of a wedged transmission cell. The result is an increase in dynamic range, but the relative intensities of absorption bands will tend to be wrong. Beer's law also will not hold. This effect is relatively mild compared with diffraction.*

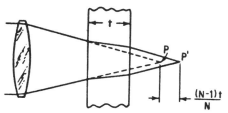

FIG. 10—*Focus shift caused by a high-index specimen. This shift occurs even if the specimen faces are perfectly parallel, and tends to be small. The effect is likely worse for the window used to support the specimen. One should aim to keep the substrate as thin and as low in refractive index as possible. For extremely critical work, the microscope should be aligned and the background run with the substrate in place (from Ref 3).*

thickness. An added complication is that the amount of shift is wavelength dependent. The longer wavelengths are bent less than the shorter ones. This is called chromatic aberration, which can add a slope to the baseline of the spectrum. This effect tends to be small with thin specimens, although care should be taken in selecting the window/support for the specimen to rest on, as this causes the same problem. Chromatic aberration is illustrated in Fig. 11.

Previously, we showed blur circles for diffraction limited optics. It is notable that the aforementioned blur circles are limited only in size by the diffraction pattern if other aberrations in the optical element are smaller than diffraction. The normal type of off-axis focussing mirror used in Fourier transform infrared (FT-IR) spectrometers and accessories, shown in Fig. 12, is not diffraction limited. An aberration called coma, which is the variation in focal length for different regions of the optic, is significant for this type of mirror. As a result, we cannot use this type of mirror in the critical areas of a microscope. The critical areas is from the specimen up to the image masking aperture. Above the image masking aperture, using the off-axis optics causes a blur at the detector. This is a radiometric problem, not a photometric one, and the result is simply that a larger detector might be required to collect the energy. Performance in the form of energy throughput suffers somewhat, but specimen purity is not compromised. Below the specimen, off-axis optics are commonly used; however, there are some benefits of using on-axis optics here also. The diffraction and stray light problems should be helped by what is called *redundant aperturing*. A variable field aperture under the specimen is closed down to the same extent as the variable aperture above the specimen. In this manner, the energy content of the lobes of the diffraction pattern is greatly reduced. In order to perform redundant aperturing, on-axis Cassegrainian optics must be used under the specimen as the condenser as well as above (the objective). Another aperture is placed at the back (slow) focus of the condenser. This adds a significant degree of complication to an infrared microscope; however, the effect is remarkable. One other type of optic which could be used is a refracting element (lens). Reflecting on-axis optics are preferred in the critical areas, as opposed to refracting elements, since chromatic aberrations from lenses would likely be above the diffraction limit.

Infrared *Ultra*microspectrometry

We have seen from this discussion that the diffraction limit is far and away the biggest hindrance to achieving good-quality infrared microspectroscopic results, *easily*. Fortunately, there is a way of achieving pure infrared spectra of features smaller than the infrared

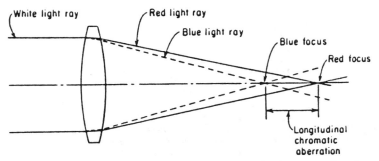

FIG. 11—*A graphic illustration of chromatic aberration. The shorter wavelengths are bent more by a given lens than are the longer wavelengths, resulting in a blurred focus (from Ref 3).*

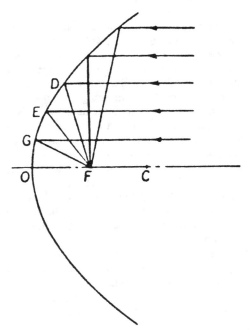

FIG. 12—*The most serious aberration for off-axis aspherical mirrors as are commonly used in FT-IR spectrometers and accessories is called "coma." This is the fact that the focal length of the mirror is dependent on the zone of the mirror; for example, ray OF has a considerably different focal length than ray DF. The effect is obviously worse for very fast mirrors. In the infrared, the blur circle due to coma is generally worse than that due to diffraction, and therefore this type of mirror cannot be used in certain critical areas of infrared microscopes (from Ref 2).*

Microspectrometry

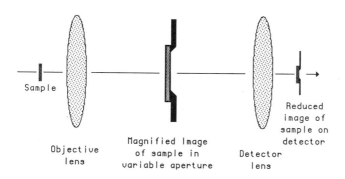

Ultramicrospectrometry

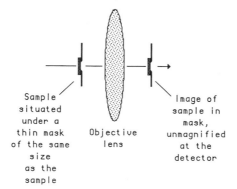

The objective lenses in these drawings
are shown as lenses for clarity. In fact,
they are really mirror assemblies.

FIG. 13—*Schematic comparison of microspectrometry and ultramicrospectrometry. In standard microspectrometry (a), an object is magnified by an objective lens or mirror assembly (shown here as a single lens) and imaged at a remote variable aperture. Another similar lens assembly re-images the object/aperture at the detector. Points outside of the specimen of interest contribute to some extent to the energy reaching the detector, even though we don't see them through the system visually. In ultramicrospectrometry, the actual-size pinhole or slit is positioned directly above the specimen in the near field (within a wavelength). Points outside of the specimen do not contribute to the energy getting through the pinhole. The pinhole/specimen is re-imaged by a lens at the detector. This image is diffracted, but at this point it causes only a blurry image at the detector, and not spectral impurity.*

diffraction limit. The tradeoff, as is often the case, is that the technique is more complicated and time-consuming. Since most specimens being analyzed today using infrared microscopes are done that way because it is the easiest way, it is troublesome to suggest that one should complicate one's life with what I am about to discuss. I would suggest that if your interest in infrared (IR) microspectrometry is purely as an "ease of use" tool, you should not consider ultramicroscopy. If, on the other hand, you deal with specimens smaller than the diffraction limit, which are sitting right next to spectrally dissimilar particles, then ultramicroscopy may be the only way to record their spectra without contamination from the neighbors. One clear application is semiconductor mapping, where features of interest are extremely small

Ultramicroscopy is a technique which was developed by visible light microscopists to see things smaller than a normal light microscope allows. Electron microscopes are normally used in these cases, but are not useful for many specimens. In ultramicroscopy, extremely small pinholes are scanned across the surface of these specimens, almost in contact with them. Since the pinhole or slit is almost directly in contact with the specimen, the light does not have a chance to spread out into a diffraction pattern. A computer stores the intensity information from each point as the specimen is scanned, and then an image is reconstructed. Pinholes as small as 30 nm have been used, well below the visible region diffraction limit. Dispersion through the pinhole now becomes a problem, but a discussion of dispersion is outside the scope of this paper.

Well, for once things work in our favor in the infrared region! We can benefit from ultramicroscopy with specimen sizes in the 1-to-50-μm range. These specimen sizes show considerable impurity radiation without ultramicroscopy, yet these sizes of pinholes are relatively easy to make. So ultramicroscopy is not as big a hassle in the infrared as it is in the visible. But the real beauty of the technique is that since the diffraction limit is much lower in the visible than in the infrared, we can actually look through these pinholes with regular microscope objectives to line up the specimen of interest. We are in a region above the visible diffraction limit, but below the infrared limit. Once we have located the specimen in the pinhole, we just switch to a detect mode and collect the spectrum. Figure 13 compares the schematic layout of standard infrared microscopy with infrared ultramicroscopy. Figure 14 indicates that there are few major differences between a standard IR microscope and one for ultra-work. Of course there is much optimization that can be done to the detector and detector optics, once we limit the field of view to a few micrometres. This will almost certainly allow *quick* acquisition of infrared spectra down to 2 μm and maybe smaller.

The current state of infrared ultramicrospectrometry is shown in Fig. 15. This is the ultramicrotransmission spectrum of polystyrene through a 5-μm ultramicro pinhole. It

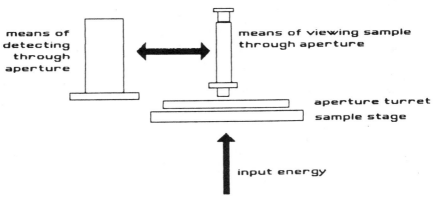

FIG. 14—*Generalized layout of an infrared ultramicrospectrometer. An aperture turret is installed directly above the specimen stage. This allows positioning and selection of apertures. A standard microscope objective is used to look down through the aperture and locate the area of interest. Then a detector is switched into place to accumulate the spectrum. It can be seen that the only necessary difference between this and a standard infrared microspectrometer is the addition of the aperture turret. Of course, optimized detector and detector optics would improve performance even further.*

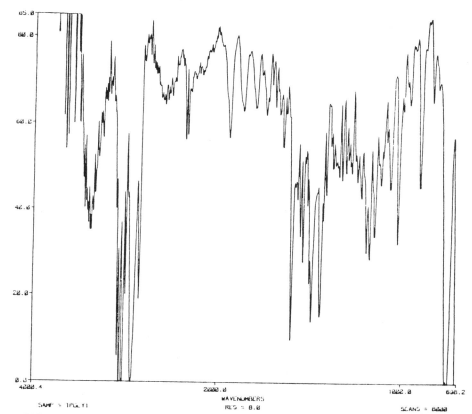

FIG. 15—*Infrared ultramicrospectrum of polystyrene obtained through a 5-µm pinhole, obtained in 8000 scans at 8 cm⁻¹ resolution. The instrumentation used here was a standard infrared microscope with a narrowband 250-µm-diameter detector. There are several aspects of this setup that are not ideal for ultramicrospectrometry, and it is believed that refinement will result in the attainment of 2-µm-diameter spectra in scans of not longer than 2 min. Most notable about this spectrum is that the bands which should go to zero do so. A remotely image-masked 5-µm speck of polystyrene film would have had a stray light component of greater than 50%.*

important to note that this spectrum is actually due to just a 5-µm-diameter spot of polystyrene film which is less than 1 ng of specimen. Because of diffraction, spectra which are obtained with remote image masking may seem to have more intensity if the specimen was larger than the spot being measured. Therefore it is important, when publishing microinfrared spectra, to state whether the system was physically masked, or remotely image masked to obtain the result. This spectrum was obtained on a commercially available infrared microscope[2] without any optimization of the detector for ultramicrospectrometry. The spectrum was collected in 8000 scans, which took about 30 min. Optimization of the detector would bring this down to a reasonable time frame. Note that this spectrum, photometrically, looks very normal. There is no stray light—all the bands which should go to zero do so.

[2] The spectrum was obtained with a Digilab FTS-60 interferometer equipped with a Digilab UMA-100 infrared microscope designed and built by Spectra-Tech, Inc., and an Infrared Associates narrow-band MCT detector with a Digilab preamplifier.

Also there is no slope, and the regions of no absorbance show up at near 100% transmission. Perhaps most importantly, had there been an infrared absorbing contaminant next to the measured 5-μm spot of polystyrene, its spectrum would not have shown up here, whereas it would have with conventional infrared microspectroscopy.

References

[1] Smith, W. J., *Modern Optical Engineering: The Design of Optical Systems*, McGraw-Hill, New York, 1966
[2] Kingslake, R. *Optical System Design*, Academic Press, New York, 1983.
[3] *Handbook of Optics*, Optical Society of America, McGraw-Hill, New York, 1978.

Bibliography

General Microscopy Reading

Clay, R. S. and Court, T. H., *The History of the Microscope*, Charles Griffin, London, (1932).

Infrared Microspectrometry Reading

Coates, V. J., Offner, O., and Siegler, E. H., Jr.,"Design and Performance of an Infrared Microscope Attachment," *Journal of the Optical Society of America*, Vol. 43, Nov. 1953. pp. 984–989.
Krishnan, K. and Kuehl, D. "A Study of the Spatial Distribution of the Oxygen Content in Silicon Wafers Using an Infrared Transmission Microscope" in *Semiconductor Processing, ASTM STP 850*, American Society for Testing and Materials, Philadelphia, 1984, pp. 325–334.
Bartick, E. G., "Microscopy/Infrared Spectroscopy For Routine Sample Sizes," *Applied Spectroscopy* Vol. 39, No. 5, Sept./Oct. 1985, pp. 885–889.
Levison, D. A., Crocker, P. R., and Allen, S. D., "Applications of Infrared Microscopy to Clinical Diagnosis," *European Spectroscopy News*, Vol. 62, 1985, pp. 18–20.
Shearer, J. C., Peters, D. C. and Kubic, T. A., "Forensic Microanalysis by Fourier Transform Infrared Spectroscopy," *Trends in Analytical Chemistry*, Vol. 4, No. 10, 1985, pp. 246–251.
Shafer, K. H., Griffiths, P. R., and Fuoco, R., "Gas Chromatography/Fourier Transform Infrared Spectrometry Under a Microscope," *Journal of High Resolution Chromatography*, Vol. 9, No. 1986, pp. 124–126.

James C. Shearer[1] and David C. Peters[2]

Fourier Transform Infrared Microspectrophotometry as a Failure Analysis Tool

REFERENCE: Shearer, J. C. and Peters, D. C., **"Fourier Transform Infrared Microspectrophotometry as a Failure Analysis Tool,"** *The Design, Sample Handling, and Applications of Infrared Microscopes, ASTM STP 949,* P. B. Roush, Ed., American Society for Testing and Materials, Philadelphia, 1987, pp. 27–38.

ABSTRACT: Recent enhancements to Fourier transform infrared (FT-IR) microsampling accessories allow sampling sizes to become vanishingly small. Using a high throughput FT-IR spectrophotometer equipped with an infrared microspectrometer accessory, we can now routinely measure specimens smaller than 10 μm in size.

With such a device, specimen presentations to the infrared (IR) beam is greatly simplified over microbeam/fixed aperture accessories. Little or no specimen preparation is required. The chemist simply places his small specimen on a small potassium bromide (KBr) window, which acts as a substrate. He then locates the region of interest in the specimen, apertures down, and analyzes the exact region in the IR as was viewed in the visible.

This paper presents recent applications of the fXA-515 FT-IR microscope accessory to industrial problems. This accessory, attached to an fX-6260 FT-IR system, was used to analyze contaminate on floppy and hard disk media. Other applications to be discussed include the analysis of defects in epoxy matrices and polarization studies of fibers.

KEY WORDS: microspectrometer, Fourier transform infrared, microsampling, infrared analysis

The advance of technology forces the development of more sophisticated analytical tools. Consider the analysis of defective transportation systems over the past one hundred years. Definition of problem: erratic forward motion due to damaged propulsion system.

1886—The cause of the problem is that the horse has a cracked hoof. The cause is easily determined by physical examination of the damaged unit. Corrective action involves first aid and then rest.

1946—The cause of the problem is a plugged fuel filter in the car's engine. Diagnosis of the problem requires a trained technician using a few simple tools, such as a screw driver and wrench. The problem can be then corrected by replacing the fuel filter (and perhaps prevented from re-occurring by installing a lockable gasoline cap to prevent children from storing dirt in car's fuel tank.)

[1] President, J. Shearer Consulting, Inc., Hamlin, NY 14464.
[2] Technical services manager, Analect Instruments, Utica, NY 13502.

1986—The cause of the problem is microscopic contamination in the bearings of a high-speed turbine pump feeding liquid hydrogen to a rocket engine. Diagnosis of the problem requires a small army of technicians who demand complete characterization of contaminants and identification of their sources. Resolution of this problem may require months of research followed by months of production modifications.

This evolution of analytical needs is inevitable (although perhaps not entirely predictable) as the ambient level of technology rises. These trends can be also followed in the field of infrared analysis.

The "standard" infrared specimen is prepared with about 1 mg of analyte in 150 mg of potassium bromide (KBr). This seems rather a modest amount, especially if one is performing a quality assurance test on a 90 720 kg (200 000 lb) lot of incoming material.

Consider, then, a situation where there is a small contaminant in a rail road car full of resin. Here the entire available specimen may be consumed in the preparation of the KBr pellet.

Next, small crystals of material are discovered on the surface of the resin pellets. Now only 1 μg of specimen is available. A useful spectrum of these crystals may still be measured by shrinking the scale of the technique. Instead of 150 mg of KBr, the specimen is dispersed in 10 mg of KBr, then the specimen is pressed into a 3-mm-diameter pellet.

Finally, there may be a few tiny specks of contamination found in the resin pellets, amounting to no more than a few nanograms each. To achieve an infrared analysis of these contaminants, a better technique than the KBr pellet will be required. This technique is simply neat analysis of the material by an infrared microscope.

During the mid-1950s, Coates et al. [1] attempted a bold approach to sampling small amounts of material with optical null, dispersive infrared spectrophotometers. They built a microscope using all reflecting optics (to eliminate problems encountered with refracting optics). They removed the detector from the monochromator and directed the infrared light into the microscope. The beam could be directed either to an eyepiece for viewing or to a thermocouple for infrared detection. The concept was valid, but the spectrophotometers of that time were not adequate for this task.

Commercial Fourier transform infrared (FT-IR) instruments appeared in the late 1960s, providing enhanced sensitivity. This enhanced performance was rapidly put to use in low optical efficiency techniques such as attenuated total reflectance (ATR) and gas chromography-infrared (GC-IR). Techniques were also developed for analysis of minute particles. When less specimen is available, the Beer-Lambert law leads one to the conclusion that adequate band intensities may be achieved by maintaining the concentration and reducing the size of the aperture. KBr pellets as small as 0.5 mm diameter may be prepared, permitting the analysis of specimens as small as 0.5 μg. With specimens smaller than this, the analyte will be contaminated by atmospheric dust during the process of grinding the material with the KBr. The obvious solution to this is to eliminate the KBr and support the specimen over the aperture by some other means. In the microscopic domain, most organic materials are sufficiently malleable that they may be flattened, placed onto a salt crystal for support, and located over an aperture 50 to 200 μm in diameter, effectively mimicking the capillary film, but with specimens of 1 to 10 ng [2,3].

This technique permits analysis of nanogram size particles, and detection of components within the particles down to the range of 100 picograms [4]. Specimens smaller than this, quite frankly, are generally too small to be the cause of a product failure. Smaller particles may be of interest in certain areas, such as the microelectronics industry, but, for most persons in the industrial sector, nanogram size specimens are the lower limit of interest.

If this is the case, then why bother with an infrared microscope? Mostly because it makes life easier. Specimens may be placed onto a standard size salt crystal, eliminating the need for tedious cleaving of crystals to form a proper mounting size, and may be directly viewed at high magnification ($\times 150$ to $\times 300$) for selection of the area of analysis. The specific area of analysis may be then selected by closing down a variable aperture which is located at an image of the specimen, rather than having to buy or make apertures. The construction of a device dedicated to microsampling also permits optimization of the detector system (also referred to as throughput matching). The result is a system capable of readily and routinely analyzing specimens at the nanogram level (and even below it).

The Analect Microscope

Although an infrared microscope is nothing more than a beam condenser with a viewing system and a beam stop aperture, the design and manufacture of such an instrument requires great attention to detail if one is to produce a unit with a high level of performance and flexibility, while maintaining an ergonomic operator interface. Figure 1 presents the optical diagram of the Analect Model XAD microscope.

The infrared light is focused at the microscope stage by means of an off-axis paraboloidal mirror, forming a spot approximately 800 μm in diameter. The paraboloid may be moved relative to the stage so that unusual sampling devices, such as a diamond anvil cell, may be utilized.

The specimen rests on a 6-mm-diameter salt crystal which is held in a metal slide on the stage. Precision micrometers permit the specimen to be moved about the viewing area, much as with any quality microscope. Options for the stage include computer controlled stage motion, heated/cooled stage, and diamond anvil cells. The Z-axis stage motion permits focusing of the specimen to the beam stop aperture (described next).

The stage is accessible from three sides so that unusual specimens or optional sampling devices may be easily mounted. Note that a cylindrical housing slides down from a Cassegrain lens (a lens composed of two mirror elements) to form a purge enclosure around the specimen. The entire microscope unit, along with the specimen stage, may be purged with dry air or nitrogen. This eliminates atmospheric absorptions due to water and carbon dioxide, which would decrease the amount of infrared energy available to interact with the specimen and decrease the overall performance of the unit.

Light transmitted through the specimen is picked up by the Cassegrain lens. This lens produces a high quality image of the specimen with $\times 15$ magnification, without the complications of chromatic aberration and limited frequency transmission of refracting lens systems. A variable aperture is placed at the image created by the Cassegrain lens. Closing this aperture permits selection of the area of analysis. Several types of apertures are available, including circular variable, a set of fixed precision pin holes, and four independent knife blades (permitting square and rectangular apertures to be formed).

The light which passes through the aperture may be directed either to a binocular viewer or to an infrared detector. Note that the infrared light beam is blocked while the microscope is in the view mode, thus preventing any stray helium-neon laser radiation coming from the interferometer from reaching the eye of the operator. A trinocular viewing head may be used by those wishing to mount a camera directly on the microscope to photograph the specimen exactly as it is analyzed.

The infrared light is passed to a liquid nitrogen cooled mercury-cadmium-telluride (MCT) detector. These detectors are available in either wideband or narrowband configurations. The wideband type covers the entire mid-infrared region from 4400 to 450 wavenumbers and provides approximately five times the sensitivity of a room temperature triglycine sulfate (TGS) detector. The narrowband type provides greater sensitivity, about 40 times more

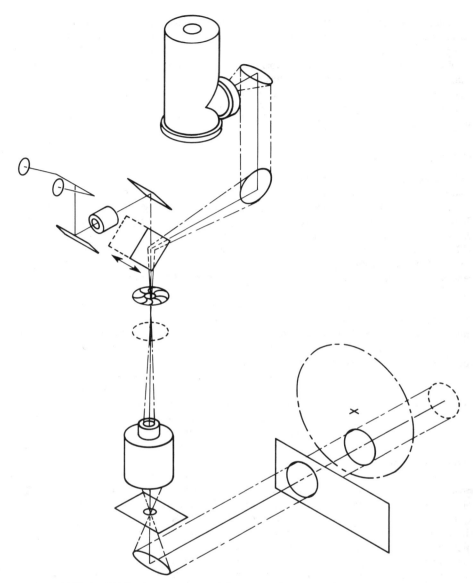

FIG. 1—*XAD microscope optical diagram with ray trace for transmission.*

than the TGS unit, but it responds only over the range of 4400 to 700 wavenumbers. One noteworthy property of infrared detectors is that noise output is proportional to the square root of the area of the detector. Since the spot of light passing through the aperture of a microscope to the detector is rather small, it makes sense to use a small area detector to minimize the noise. This is what is meant by "throughput matching." The XAD microscope uses an MCT detector with a 0.25 by 0.25 mm crystal for optimum performance.

The XAD microscope also offers a specular reflectance mode. This sampling configuration is extremely useful for analysis of contaminants on electrical contacts and defects in coatings over metallic substrates. "Bulk" type specimens, such as defects in a sheet of polymer, are rarely amenable to specular reflectance, due to low first surface reflectance from specimens of low refractive index. The optical diagram in Fig. 2 shows the reflectance sampling mode. For reasons of efficiency, the infrared beam is apertured at a conjugate focal plane and then injected into the Cassegrain lens by a spatial separation technique.

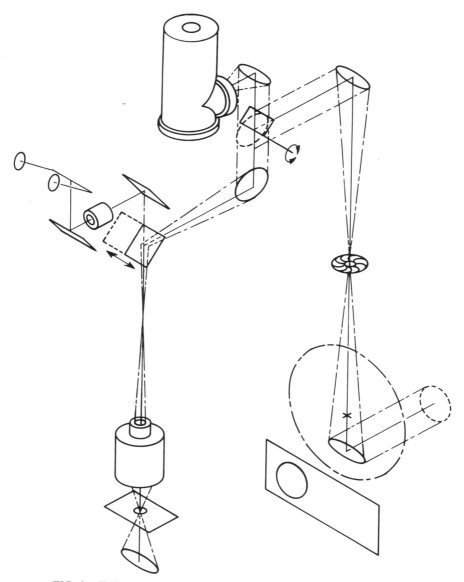

FIG. 2—*XAD microscope optical diagram with ray trace for reflectance.*

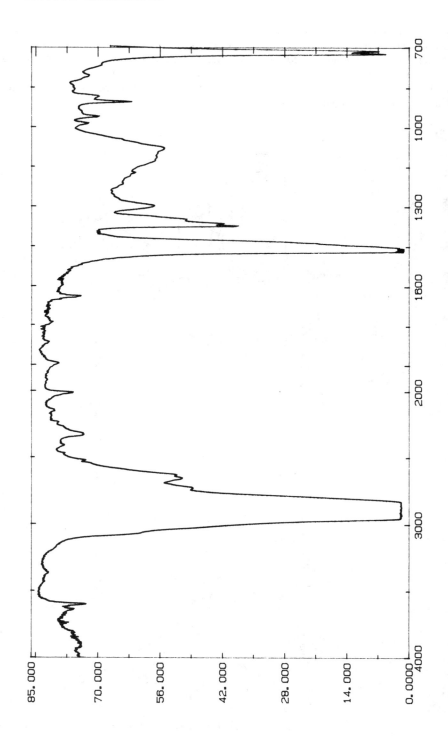

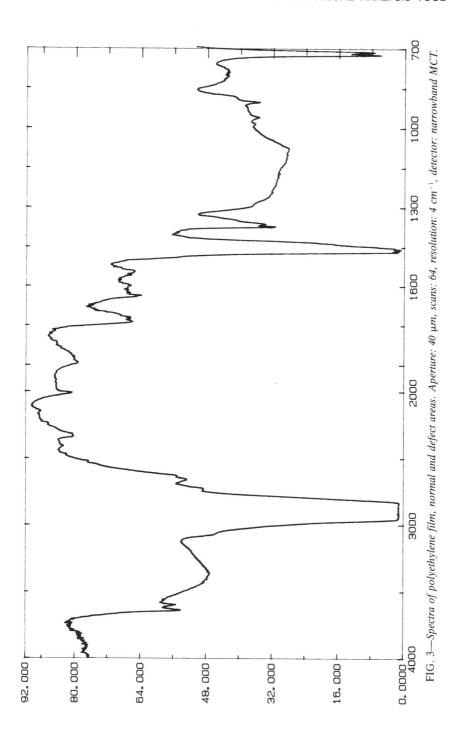

FIG. 3—*Spectra of polyethylene film, normal and defect areas. Aperture: 40 µm, scans: 64, resolution: 4 cm^{-1}, detector: narrowband MCT.*

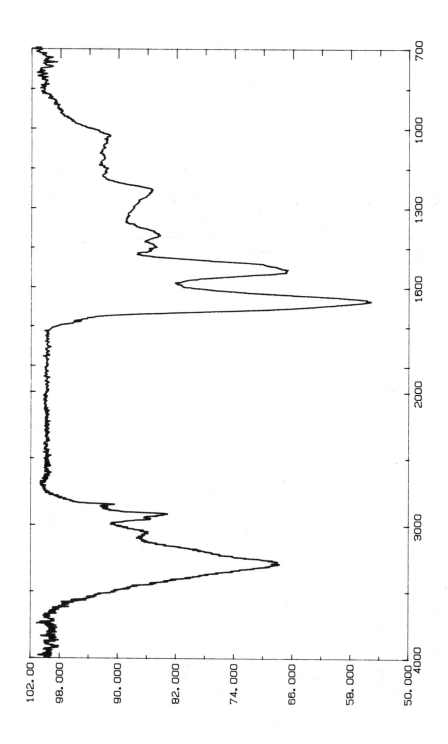

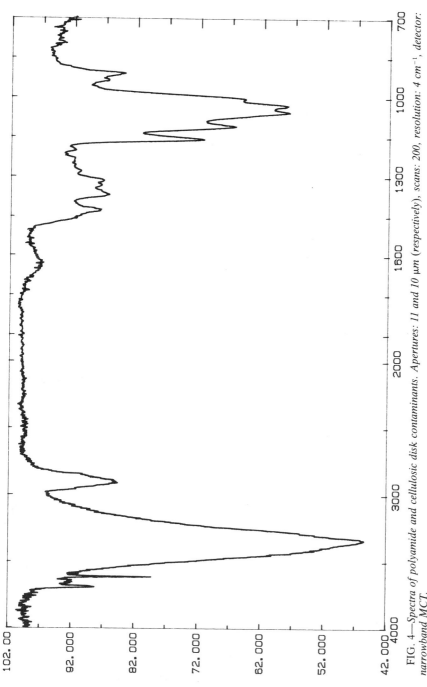

FIG. 4—*Spectra of polyamide and cellulosic disk contaminants. Apertures: 11 and 10 μm (respectively), scans: 200, resolution: 4 cm⁻¹, detector: narrowband MCT.*

Tools Required

To prepare specimens for microanalysis, a few simple tools are necessary. The first o these is a stereo-zoom microscope. Any microscopist will tell you that there are many type of microscopes, and each has its purpose. The infrared microscope provides high magnifi cation of the specimen to enable areas as small as 10 μm in diameter to be selected fo analysis. This means that the infrared microscope has a very limited field of view (how fa you can see side to side) and a limited depth of field (how far up and down you can see due to specimen falling out of focus). To prepare a specimen for infrared analysis, it is mucl easier to work under a stereo-zoom microscope at magnifications of 10 to ×50.

To isolate and manipulate specimens, only a few relatively inexpensive tools are needed While it is possible to spend thousands of dollars on custom designed microtools, mos analysts get by quite nicely with a fine pointed probe, very fine pointed forceps, and . scalpel (or even just a razor blade).

The cheapest way to get a fine pointed probe is to buy a package of dissecting needle and sharpen the tip on 400 and 600 grit sandpaper. If the specimen in question is to b examined for elemental composition (by electron microprobe, for example), then a tungste: wire probe should be used. Iron, as found in the dissecting needle probe, is a fairly commo: type of contamination. Tungsten, however, is rarely encountered as either a component o a contaminant in organic chemicals or polymeric systems. If one uses a tungsten probe t prepare the specimen, and tungsten is later found in the elemental analysis, one is reasonabl certain that the tungsten came from the probe, and was not part of the original specimer If, on the other hand, one uses a steel probe and then finds iron in the specimen, it i impossible to know whether the iron was present in the original specimen or if it came fro: the probe during specimen preparation.

The best choice for forceps are very fine pointed, stainless steel dissecting forceps. / good pair will cost $15 to $20, but they are well worth the money. Keep these close guarded, however, as other laboratory personnel, unaware of their proper care, will try t use them for removing slivers from their fingers or to pry small objects out of tight place:

A sharp, clean blade is often useful when trying to excise contaminants from within object: The most common choice here is a scalpel, perferably a No. 3 handle with a No. 11 blad. This blade provides a long, straight cutting edge and a fine tip. Some may prefer a singl edge razor blade, either for economic or aesthetic reasons. When using a razor blade, b sure to wash the blade with solvent before using it, as the blades come with an oil coatir to prevent them from rusting.

Remember that the goal of specimen preparation is to flatten the material such that th area selected for analysis is thin (1 to 5 μm) and uniform. Round specimens, such as fiber may give identifiable spectra when analyzed without modification, but for best result flattening the specimen will provide higher quality data, permitting quantitative manipu lations, like absorbance subtractions, to be performed. The circular shape of the fiber objectionable for two reasons. First, the specimen will act like a lens, defocusing the lig and decreasing optical efficiency. Second, the circular shape is a photometric disaster; t thick at the center and too thin at the edge. A simple tap with the side of the probe w suffice to flatten the fiber. Most other organic materials may be similarly treated, sin things which seem on the macroscopic scale to be hard, are really quite malleable on microscopic scale.

Typical Examples

The most straight forward type of specimen is a thin polymer film. In this case, t problem involved gel slugs or inclusions in a polyethylene film. No specimen preparatic

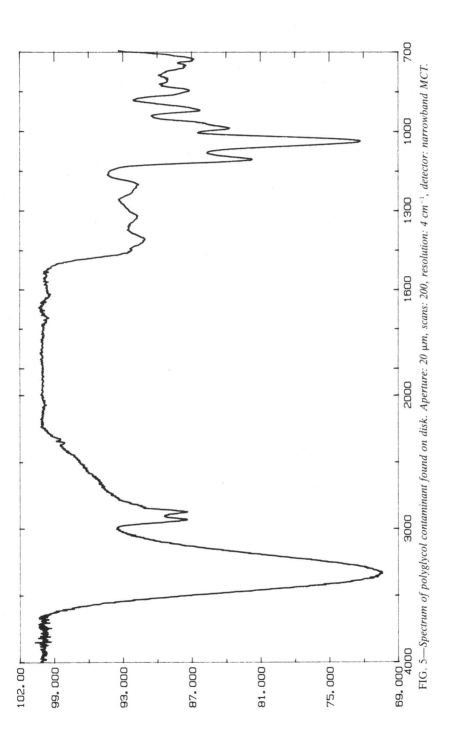

FIG. 5—*Spectrum of polyglycol contaminant found on disk. Aperture: 20 μm, scans: 200, resolution: 4 cm⁻¹, detector: narrowband MCT.*

was required, as the film was of suitable thickness for direct infrared measurement. A portion of the film was placed onto the stage of the XAD microscope, and the aperture was closed down so that only one of the defects could be seen. Switching to the test mode, the infrared spectrum of the viewed area was collected. This was compared with the spectrum from normal area of the film. Figure 3 shows the spectra from the defect and normal areas. Bands due to —OH, —C=O, and —C—O— indicate that the material in the defect areas has suffered oxidative degradation.

The second example is a series of contaminants found on magnetic disks during manufacturing. The first disk has two contaminant particles, one in the recording area of the disk and the other on the hub area. The particles are only 8 and 11 μm in size, and appear similar on visual examination. The infrared spectra of these particles (Fig. 4) show them to be quite different. The first is cellulosic, with some Kaolin clay. This is probably from a coated paper used in the manufacturing process. The second is a polyamide, which closely matches the Nylon resin used in the disk package.

A second magnetic disk had a small (20 μm diameter) droplet of liquid near the edge. The spectrum of this specimen (Fig. 5) appears similar to that of a polyglycol, much like the material used to disperse the iron oxide over the surface of the disk.

Conclusions

While many debate the theoretical performance limits of infrared microscopes, the potential for solving numerous, everyday industrial problems, formerly impossible or extremely difficult, is now swift, efficient, and routine.

Acknowledgments

The authors wish to thank Neil Spingarn, S&N Laboratories, for providing the spectra of disk contaminants.

References

[1] Coates, V. J., Offner, A., and Siegler, E. H., Jr., *Journal of the Optical Society of America,* Vol. 43, p. 984.
[2] Cournoyer, R., Shearer, J. C., and Anderson, D. H., *Analytical Chemistry,* Vol. 49, p. 2275.
[3] Shearer, J. C., Peters, D. C., Hoepfner, J., and Newton, T., *Analytical Chemistry,* Vol. 55, p. 874A.
[4] Cournoyer, R., Shearer, J. C., and Anderson, D. H., *Analytical Chemistry,* Vol. 49, p. 2275.

Howard J. Humecki[1]

Specimen Preparation for Microinfrared Analysis

REFERENCE: Humecki, H. J., "**Specimen Preparation for Microinfrared Analysis,**" *The Design, Sample Handling, and Applications of Infrared Microscopes, ASTM STP 949*, P. B. Roush, Ed., American Society for Testing and Materials, Philadelphia, 1987, pp. 39–48.

ABSTRACT: Improved sensitivity of detectors and more powerful computers have extended the useful limits of infrared spectroscopy downward to the nanogram level. The analyst must adopt the techniques of the microscopist in preparing these tiny specimens for analysis if he is to take full advantage of these advances. Some techniques are described for dealing with small specimens, including transferring nanolitre quantities of liquids to a salt window and preparing spectra pyrolyzates from filled and pigmented polymer specimens of less than 1 μg.

KEY WORDS: infrared microspectroscopy, infrared spectrometers, microscopes (optical), polymer analysis, polymer pyrolysis

During the past five to ten years, tremendous advances have been achieved in infrared spectroscopy. Instrument designers and manufacturers have used components and materials from the semiconductor, optics, and laser industries as well as developments in the computer and software industries. Microinfrared techniques have progressed from the use of beam condensers and pinhole apertures to sophisticated microscopes with surface reflecting lens systems.

The limits of microinfrared analysis have changed from milligrams to nanograms. In the horizon are advances that will extend our limits to the picogram range in perhaps five to ten years. The hardware we use for generating spectra has certainly improved and will continue to improve. Can we say the same for methods we use to prepare our specimens? Probably not!

We are on the fringes of truly microinfrared capabilities but have not taken full advantage of microscopical sample handling techniques. This area will rapidly become a limiting factor in our ability to characterize small specimens. Commonly, specimen preparation consists of smearing a dab of goo or placing a particle on a salt plate and letting high technology take care of the rest. Some simple techniques will help an analyst obtain more and better information from tiny specimens.

Apparatus

The spectrometer used for these studies was a Digilab Model FTS-20C infrared spectrophotometer. It was modified to accept a 30-year-old Perkin Elmer Model 85 microscope accessory. The microscope was from an era when a microinfrared specimen was 1 by 4 mm in size. The source was the standard Digilab glow bar. The microscope and spectrophotometer as shown in Fig. 1. The detector (on the right) was an MCT detector. The optical path, shown in Fig. 2, consists of a substage Cassegrainian optic approximately 10 cm in diameter

---

[1] Senior research chemist, McCrone Associates, Inc., Westmont, IL 60559.

FIG. 1—*Spectrophotometer equipped with microscope.*

that focuses the beam to a spot about 2 mm in diameter in the center of the adjustable stage. The system is capable of recording spectra of particles as small as 10 to 20 μm in diameter. It is worth mentioning that obtaining a spectrum of a particle 20 μm in size is not the same as aperturing to 20 μm on a larger specimen. The lower recorded energy on small, individual specimens is probably caused by edge effects and surface scatter on the small particles, and large acceptance angles through an aperture on large specimens.

Small specimens can be picked up and transferred with tungsten needles sharpened to extremely fine points. Figure 3 shows a sharpened tungsten needle compared with a standard dissecting needle tip. It is clear that a 25-μm-diameter flake or particle would be lost on the tip of a sewing or dissecting needle, whereas it could easily be found and manipulated with the fine 1- to 3-μm tip of the tungsten needle. A tungsten needle can be prepared by heating the tip of a tungsten wire to red heat in a burner and then quickly drawing it through a melted spot on a stick of sodium nitrite. Use a 3-cm length of 24 to 26 gage (0.5 mm) tungsten wire fitted into a wire loop holder approximately 12 cm in length. Other methods are available for preparing needles but this is the simplest [1]. A stereomicroscope is very useful for observing the particles while manipulation is being carried out because of the three-dimensional view as well as the long-working distances.

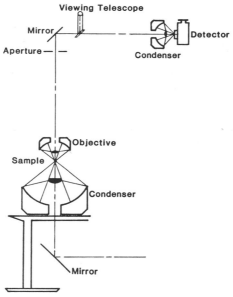

FIG. 2—*Microscope optical path.*

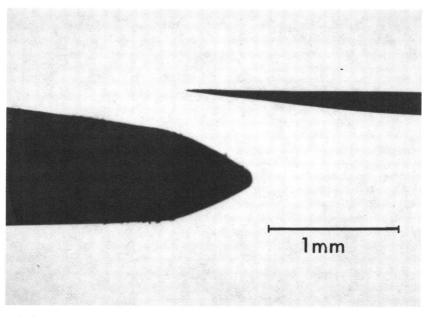

FIG. 3—*Sharpened tungsten needle* (upper) *compared with standard sewing needle.*

Preparation Technique

Figure 4 shows a section of heart tissue under slightly uncrossed polars. Two types of surgical thread (approximately 20 μm in diameter) can be observed: one is birefringent and the other isotropic. A cross section of each type of thread was removed with a tungsten needle and pressed between two steel plates. The pressing of these specimens offers two advantages: the specimen's diameter is increased and the thickness is decreased. Both of these improve spectral quality. Figures 5a and b show the two spectra obtained. One has been identified as a tetrafluoroethylene resin type material and the other a polypropylene.

A particle was removed from a nozzle and examined with an optical microscope. Although it was suspected of being cellulosic, it was so damaged by abrasion that its identifying characteristics were blurred. Therefore, polarized light microscopy, which can generally be used to identify wood and cotton fibers, was unsuccessful. When the specimen was pressed and an infrared spectrum obtained, it was easily identified as being cellulosic.

A crystalline substance developed in an isotropic film. These crystals could not be readily removed by a simple surgical procedure without fragmentation, consequently, it was nec essary to analyze them *in situ*. Because they were similar in refractive index to the matrix they could only be observed between crossed polars with an optical microscope. The infrared microscope attachment has no features for polarized light examination, consequently, crys tals could not be directly observed with the microscope attachment. In order to locate these crystals in the infrared beam, a polarizer was taped over the optical light source and an analyzer was placed above the specimen in a slightly uncrossed position. The crystal could easily be observed and was positioned and apertured correctly for analysis. By subtracting a matrix spectrum from that of the crystal in the matrix, the contaminant was readily identified as a long-chain amide used as an antistatic compound.

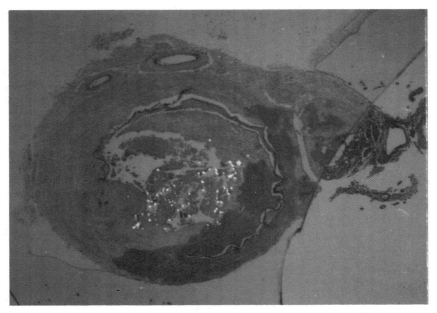

FIG. 4—*Cross section of heart tissue under slightly uncrossed polars. Bright spots are birefringent thread cross sections.*

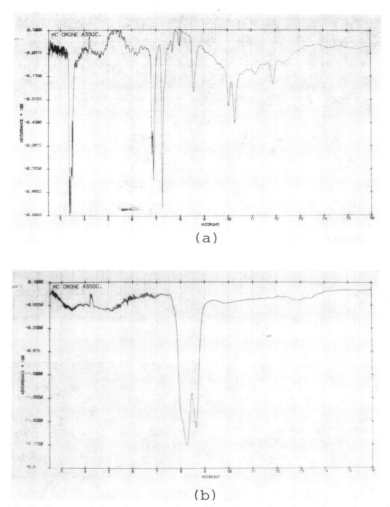

FIG. 5—*Spectra of thread cross sections:* (a) *polypropylene* (b) *polytetrafluoroethylene.* 1024 scans at resolution of 8 cm⁻¹.

An aggravating problem when dealing with elastomers is that they tend to form a ball. The result is that the specimen is too thick and useful spectra cannot be obtained. The problem can be solved by placing the elastomeric specimen on a salt plate and pressing it down with another piece of polished salt. While the specimen is in this position, a quick setting adhesive such as Duco® is applied to the edge of the salt plates and allowed to dry while the elastomer is in the flat position. Figure 6 shows such a specimen after preparation.

The presence of fillers and pigments in insoluble polymer matrices can usually be handled by pyrolyzing the specimen and obtaining a spectrum of the pyrolysis products. The difficulty arises when only tiny specimens are available. By employing a device which we call a capillary brush, we have been able to extend the technique to specimens less than 1 μg in size.

Figure 7 shows a capillary brush of 200 μm inside diameter in various stages of manu-

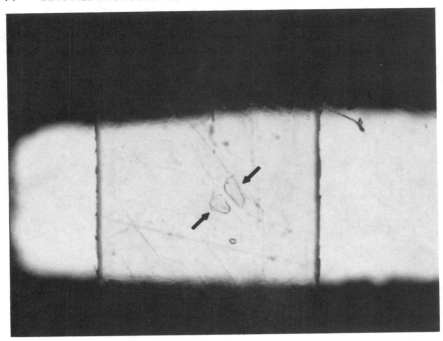

FIG. 6—*Elastomer pressed between two salt plates.*

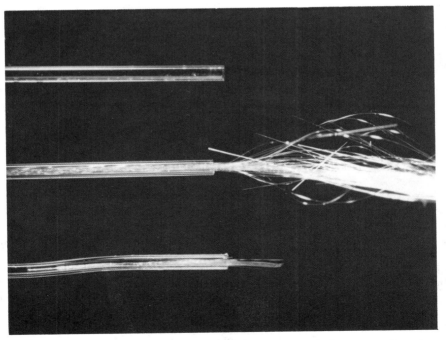

FIG. 7—*Preparation of capillary brush:* (top) *200* μm *outside diameter capillary;* (center) *borosilicate glass wool inserted into capillary; and,* (bottom) *finished capillary brush.*

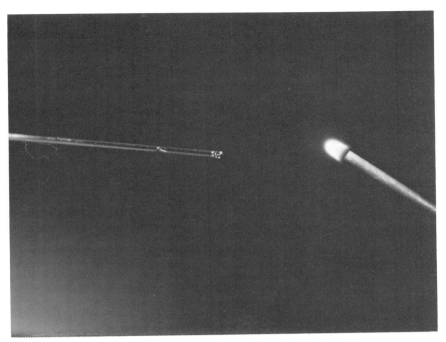

FIG. 8—*Pyrolyzing the particle in the closed capillary.*

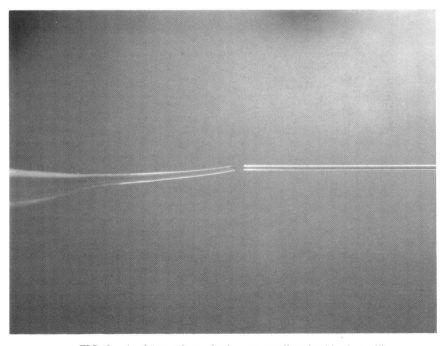

FIG. 9—*Applying a drop of solvent to capillary* (end broken off).

facture. The upper image is of the end of a 200-μm by 10-cm-long borosilicate glass capillary. The second image is that of a capillary after some borosilicate glass wool has been stuffed into the end. The next step in the production of the capillary brush requires the use of a hobbist microtorch to fuse the borosilicate glass wool to the sides of the capillary. The bottom figure shows the capillary after it has been trimmed with a pair of scissors. Ultrasonicating the capillaries in suitable solvents cleans the brush as well as removes loose particles from the glass fibers.

In use, the particle to be pyrolyzed is inserted into the end of the capillary opposite the brush. It should be pushed into the tube about 2 to 3 mm with a small wire. The tube end is sealed with the microtorch and the flame is then played along the tube until the specimen is pyrolyzed (Fig. 8). Observation with the stereomicroscope shows many tiny droplets of pyrolyzate on the sides of the tube a very short distance from the ash left by the pyrolysis procedure. After breaking off the tip containing the ash, a droplet of solvent is applied to the end of the tube as shown in Fig. 9. The pyrolyzate, washed down by the solvent, reaches the brush tip and the tip is gently touched to the salt plate (Fig. 10). By repeatedly touching the brush tip to the salt plate, the pyrolyzate can be constrained to an area 200 μm or less

FIG. 10—*Applying pyrolyzate solution to salt plate.*

in diameter. Because the solvent quantity is very low, drying is usually accomplished simply by the heat from the microscope lamp.

Figure 11 shows the reproducibility achieved with this process on a clay-filled epoxy putty. The reproducibility is better than is generally achieved with larger specimens. This is attributed to two factors: (1) pyrolysis is almost instantaneous and thus takes place in a more reproducible manner, and (2) the entire specimen is washed down the capillary and deposited on the salt plate. This eliminates the potential for analyzing a portion of a fractionated

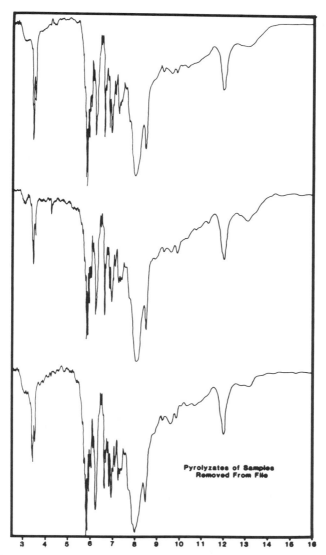

FIG. 11—*Spectra of three submicrogram specimens, showing reproducibility. 1024 scans at resolution of 8 cm^{-1}.*

pyrolyzate. The capillary brush can also be used to transfer small quantities of solvent soluble contaminants from specimen surfaces. A microdroplet of solvent is placed on the contaminant and immediately it is contacted with a clean capillary brush which removes the solvent and solute. This is repeated several times. The "loaded" brush is then touched repeatedly to the surface of a clean salt plate. As the solvent evaporates on the plate, the contaminant is deposited in a restricted area for analysis with the microinfrared spectrophotometer.

Conclusion

In conclusion, we have shown some techniques that are of value for preparing small specimens for microinfrared analysis. As technology improves, the limiting factor in our ability to analyze microscopic specimens will not depend on instrumentation but on our ability to properly prepare small specimens for analysis.

Reference

[1] McCrone, W. C. and Delly, J. G., The Particle Atlas, 2nd ed., Ann Arbor Science Publishers, Ann Arbor, MI, Vol. 1, 1973, pp. 225–227.

J. E. Katon,[1] Patricia L. Lang,[1] D. W. Schiering,[2] and J. F. O'Keefe[3]

Instrumental and Sampling Factors in Infrared Microspectroscopy

REFERENCE: Katon, J. E., Lang, P. L., Schiering, D. W., and O'Keefe, J. F., **"Instrumental and Sampling Factors in Infrared Microspectroscopy,"** *The Design, Sample Handling, and Applications of Infrared Microscopes, ASTM STP 949,* P. B. Roush, Ed., American Society for Testing and Materials, Philadelphia, 1987, pp. 49–63.

ABSTRACT: Infrared microspectroscopy is an emerging technical field of great promise. As with all new fields, there are experimental techniques and applications specifically related to this field. This paper discusses some general features and experimental techniques for use with a commercial infrared microspectrometer as applied to fiber identification. It then discusses a specially constructed infrared microscope which may be utilized with specialized accessories, diamond anvil cells, to generally and easily obtain infrared spectra of specimens which are initially too thick.

KEY WORDS: infrared microspectroscopy, identification of microscopic particles

The Molecular Microspectroscopy Laboratory (MML) was designed and established at Miami University to carry out research in the newly emerging field of molecular microspectroscopy, especially in the vibrational spectroscopies. This paper describes some recent results obtained and techniques developed while carrying out two different research projects underway at MML. The first is the rapid identification of small single fibers by infrared microspectroscopy and utilizes a commercial infrared microspectrometer system, the Analect AQS-20M system. The second addresses the very general problem of excessive specimen pathlength in infrared microspectroscopy. It is shown that specimens which give this problem may be quickly and easily studied utilizing a diamond anvil cell (DAC) [1,2] in conjunction with a custom-built and designed infrared microscope possessing a long-working distance and widely variable focus.

Experimental

The Analect AQS-20M system in our laboratory consists of an Analect fX-6260 Fourier transform infrared spectrophotometer (FT-IR) and an Analect fXA-515 microscope module. The objective lens of the fXA-515 is a ×15 Cassegrainian, and a variable-diameter circular aperture is mounted in the focal plane. The mercury cadmium telluride narrowband detector has an area of 0.50 mm² and is responsive to about 700 cm⁻¹. The unit operates in the transmission mode only. It should be noted that although a circular aperture has certain

[1] Professor of chemistry and director, Molecular Microspectroscopy Laboratory, and doctoral student, respectively, Department of Chemistry, Miami University, Oxford, OH 45056.
[2] Perkin-Elmer Corporation, Norwalk, CT 06859-0903.
[3] Copeland Corporation, Sydney, OH 45365.

FIG. 1—*Custom-built infrared microscope accessory.*

advantages for general purpose studies, it is not the ideal for studying fibers. A variable size rectangular aperture would be better suited for such specimens.

The custom-built infrared microscope is pictured in Fig. 1, and a simplified block diagram is given in Fig. 2. Both the condenser and objective are ×15 Cassegrainian lenses. Both are adjustable for focusing at any point within an approximately 10-cm working distance. The unit has a dedicated wide-band MCT detector whose active element has an area of 1.0 mm². It is sensitive to about 425 cm⁻¹. It operates with a variable-diameter circular aperture which is mounted ahead of the condenser lens. The outside case of the microscope has been constructed so that it fits the specimen compartment of a Digilab FTS-14 C/D FT-IR, which is used for all studies.

Raman spectra were recorded on an Instruments SA, Inc. Ramanor U-1000 Raman Microspectrometer fitted with objectives of different magnifying power.

The DACs are commercial models available from High Pressure Diamond Optics, Inc. Figure 3 illustrates the high-pressure diamond cell. The diamonds have faces about 0.4 mm in diameter, and they are about 0.8 mm thick. Although capable of exerting pressures in the kilobars, such pressures are not needed for most specimens. Figure 4 illustrates the low to moderate-pressure cell. The diamonds here are about 0.7 mm in diameter and perhaps 0.4 mm thick. Although not capable of exerting such high pressures, this cell is more convenient to use and requires less space within the microscope. Another advantage is

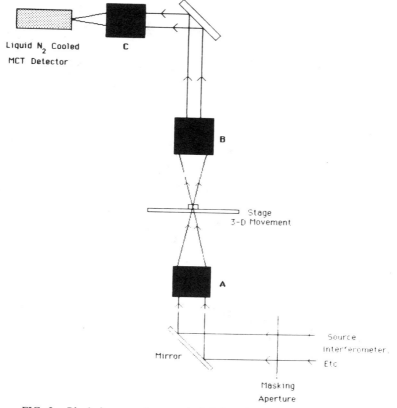

FIG. 2—*Block diagram of custom-built infrared microscope accessory.*

illustrated in Fig. 5, which shows the infrared spectra of Type II diamonds, of which both cells are constructed. The two spectra, A and B, were not taken with these cells, but they illustrate the point. The diamonds in the high-pressure cell are sufficiently thick that they are totally absorbing in the 1900 to 2000 cm^{-1} range. However, this is not true of the diamonds in the lower-pressure cell. The diamond absorption can be subtracted from spectra obtained with this cell. The absorption is not in a particularly troublesome region, but it is, nevertheless, convenient to compensate for it.

Results and Discussion

Fiber Identification

Figure 6 is a photomicrograph of three single fibers which are typical of those studied. The cotton and acrylic fibers are both about 12 μm wide and the portion of the wool fiber is about 18 μm wide. The cotton and wool specimens are both rather flat and are therefore probably 5 to 10 μm thick; the acrylic is about 12 μm thick since it is a cylindrical fiber. Many fibers are thicker than these, but it is unusual to find thinner ones. Figure 7 compares the infrared spectrum of the single cotton fiber with that of a bundle of cotton fibers. The

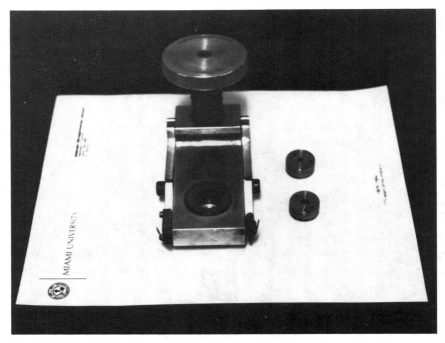

FIG. 3—*High-pressure diamond cell.*

FIG. 4—*Moderate-pressure diamond cell.*

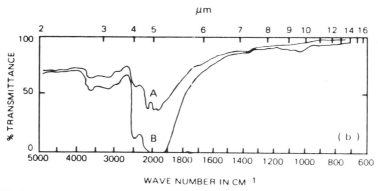

FIG. 5—*Infrared spectra of type II diamonds* (A *and* B *represent specimen thickness difference only*).

fiber diameter corresponds, of course, to the wavelength of the radiation being utilized. One would expect rather severe diffraction effects with such a specimen. Although the spectrum of the single fiber is noisy, it corresponds very well to that obtained with the larger specimen. Some spectral resolution is lost, but the spectrum is clearly that of cotton and would serve quite satisfactorily for identification. It should be noted that this spectrum consists of 300 scans, which corresponds to a recording time of about five minutes. Each of the succeeding spectra of fibers was recorded with this same number of scans.

Figure 8 compares the spectra of the cotton fiber with that of the wool fiber. The spectra are quite different, making differentiation of these fibers relatively easy. Note, however, that the greater width of the wool fiber is reflected by a spectrum with a considerably improved signal/noise ratio. Diffraction effects would be expected to be considerably lessened in this case since its width is now greater than the wavelength of the infrared radiation. This is actually true, as the spectra clearly show upon comparison. Figure 9 shows the spectrum of the acrylic fiber. Again, the fiber diameter is about 12-μm but the signal/noise ratio is considerably poorer in this case than with the cotton. This is due to the defocusing of the infrared beam by the cylindrical shape of the fiber. The fiber acts as a small lens and defocuses the beam so that a significant amount of energy is lost. Note that even though the spectrum is quite noisy, it is sufficiently clear that at least routine identification can be carried out. Of course, the spectral quality could be improved by increasing the number of signal averaged scans, but this would require more sampling time.

We have acquired the infrared spectra of a large number of synthetic and natural fibers and find that their infrared spectra are quite distinctive and lend themselves to rapid identification of the fiber. Classical methods of fiber identification are either more time-consuming or are subjective and lack some specificity [3,4]. Although the reference spectra we have were all recorded from fibers a few millimetres in length, this size is far larger than necessary. The length need only be about 10 μm, as is indicated from these spectra. Such small specimens can be troublesome since they are lightweight and easily carried away by air currents. We have found a convenient method of fixing them using commercial rubber cement which has been diluted 1:1 with cyclohexane. A thin, even film of this diluted cement is placed on the specimen support and the particle placed on top of it. In a few seconds the specimen is firmly attached. A background spectrum of the rubber cement is taken about

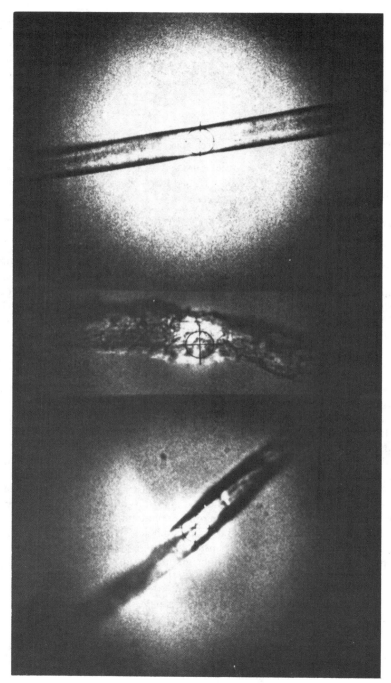

FIG. 6—*Photomicrographs of cotton* (left), *wool* (center) *and acrylic* (right) *fibers.*

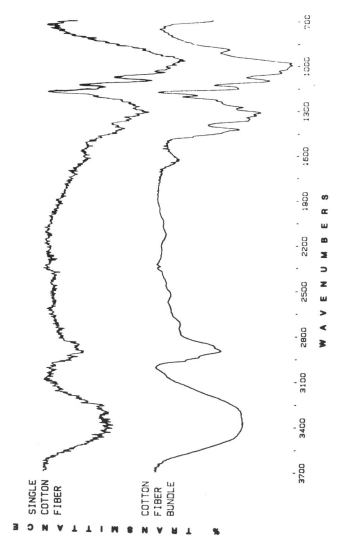

FIG. 7—*Infrared spectra of single cotton fiber (top) and cotton fiber bundle (bottom).*

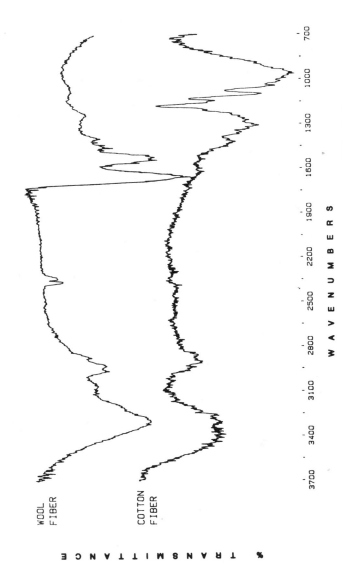

FIG. 8—*Infrared spectra of single cotton fiber (bottom) and single wool fiber (top).*

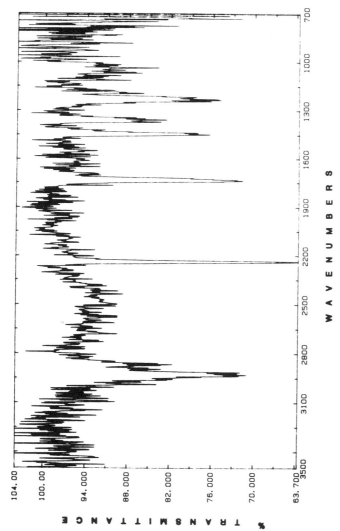

FIG. 9—*Infrared spectrum of acrylic fiber.*

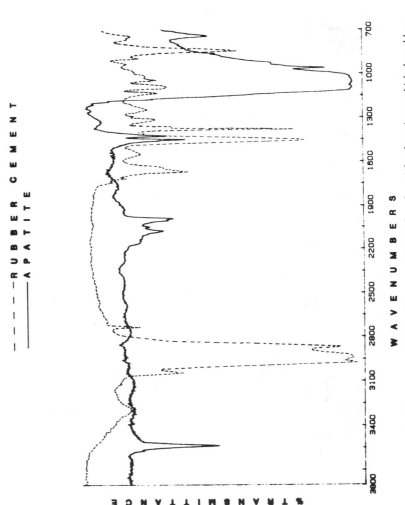

FIG. 10—*Infrared spectrum of dried rubber cement (dotted) and particle of apatite to which the rubber cement spectrum has been ratioed (solid).*

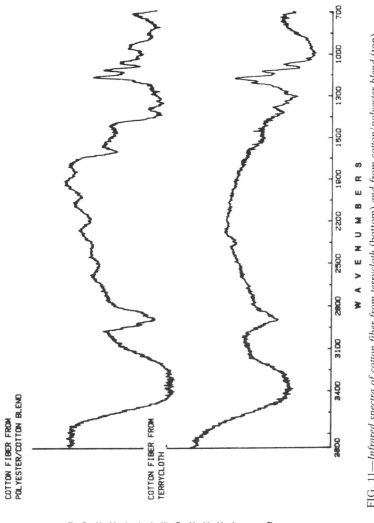

FIG. 11—*Infrared spectra of cotton fiber from terrycloth* (bottom) *and from cotton/polyester blend* (top).

10 μm from the specimen. The results are illustrated in Fig. 10, which shows the background spectrum of the rubber cement as a dotted line and the spectrum of a small particle of apatite (calcium fluorophosphate) attached to the rubber cement, *after* ratioing to the background. It is clear from the 3000 to 2800 cm^{-1} region that the ratioing procedure is very effective in removing the rubber cement spectrum. The film of rubber cement bearing the particle may then be stripped off of the specimen support for subsequent experiments.

Secondary differences in fibers are also easily detected in many cases. Figure 11 compares the cotton terry fiber with a cotton fiber separated from a cotton/polyester blend thread of which a fabric was composed. It is evident that the cotton in the cotton/polyester blend has been treated in some way such that it gives a distinctly different spectrum. Note that the spectrum is not that of acetate, which one might think at first glance. Acetate gives a definitely different spectrum than either of these fibers. (Acetate is made from cellulose triacetate by the hydrolysis of 0.5 to 1.0 acetyl group per glucose unit. Cellulose triacetate is still another fiber which gives, again, its own characteristic spectrum.) The new bands in the spectrum probably arise from a polyurethane finish. Such finishes are commonly applied to improve cotton's wrinkle recovery properties. It is also possible to differentiate different dyes on fibers by the observed infrared spectrum of the single fiber. This work has not been completed as yet, so definitive quantitative statements cannot be made at this time.

As an aside, we might note that these fibers often show the well-known complementarity of infrared and Raman spectra. Figure 12 compares a portion of both spectra of a 17-μm diameter synthetic fiber. The Raman spectrum shows very clearly the unsaturation present in the fiber, which is not apparent from the infrared spectrum. This fiber can be identified readily as an aromatic polyester (probably Dacron) even without reference spectra. Further structural details could be obtained from a more detailed comparison of the spectra. For instance, the 142 cm^{-1} band is due to anatase titanium dioxide (TiO$_2$), a common delustrant for synthetic fibers.

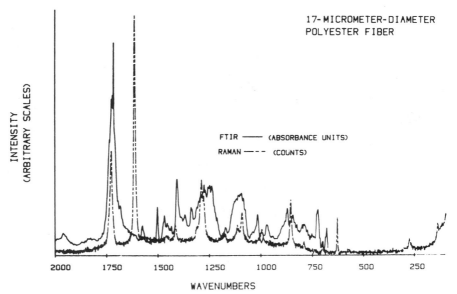

FIG. 12—*Infrared and Raman spectra of 17-μm-diameter synthetic fiber.*

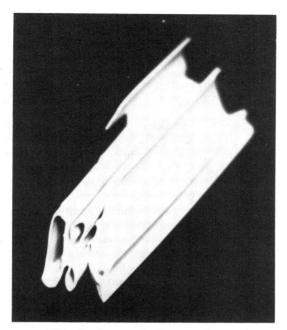

FIG. 13—*Portion of refrigerator door gasket.*

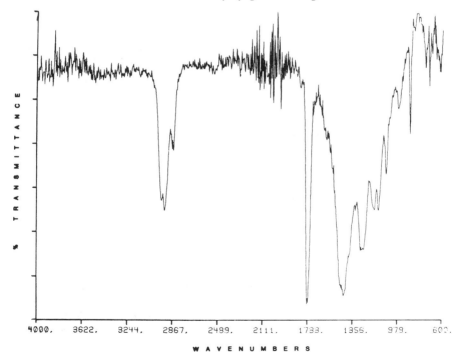

FIG. 14—*Infrared spectrum of specimen in Fig. 13 as taken with moderate-pressure diamond cell.*

Diamond Anvil Cell Utilization

One of the most troubling aspects of infrared microspectroscopy is specimen thickness. As a rule of thumb, 10-to-15-μm pathlength of a pure material gives good spectral representation, although the exact pathlength does depend on the material, of course. It is not unusual to have specimens whose thickness is too great, and a quick sampling accessory is therefore quite desirable. The diamond pressure cells available from High Pressure Diamond Optics fill this need admirably.

There are currently two difficulties encountered when attempting to use these cells with commercial infrared microscope accessories: (1) they require a rather longer working distance than is often available, and (2) they require more flexible focusing arrangements than is normally available. For this reason, we have acquired the custom-designed and built infrared microscope accessory and fitted it to our Digilab FTS-14 C/D FT-IR.

Figure 13 is a picture of a specimen which we have recently studied using this microscope and the moderate-pressure diamond cell. The specimen is a part of a gasket for a refrigerator door and is heavily plasticized and filled polyvinyl chloride. The notched portion has a thickness of 0.83 mm and has irregularities whose chemical nature was of interest. A spectrum of a smooth portion of the material obtained with the moderate-pressure cell (about 3 min specimen preparation time, 500 scans) is shown in Fig. 14.

Figure 15 shows a small piece of nylon fishing line, 428 μm in diameter. The indention was caused by the high-pressure diamond cell, which was used to obtain the spectrum, again with less than 5 min specimen preparation time. This thickness of nylon was too great for the moderate-pressure cell. The spectrum obtained is shown in Fig. 16 (1444 scans).

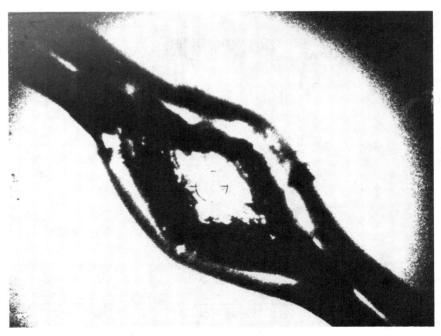

FIG. 15—*Nylon fishing line after insertion in high-pressure diamond cell.*

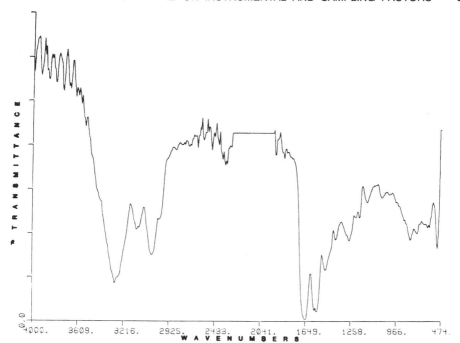

FIG. 16—*Infrared spectrum of specimen in Fig.15 as taken with high pressure diamond cell.*

Conclusions

The emerging field of infrared microspectroscopy shows great potential for molecular identification of very small specimens. As an example, it is shown that very small bits of fibers may be identified quickly and easily by infrared microspectroscopy as compared to the much more tedious and subjective microscope methods used classically. Because even very small specimens may be too thick for satisfactory spectra to be obtained, a convenient method of pressing them into thinner sections is needed. The diamond anvil cells do this readily with no chance of specimen loss. As an additional benefit, the thinning of the specimen increases its diameter. Thus a particle about 10 μm in diameter may be 20 to 30 μm in diameter after pressing. This, of course, yields a much better spectrum since diffraction effects are essentially removed.

References

[1] Lippincott, E. R., Weir, C. E., VanValkenburg, A., and Bunting, E. N., *Spectrochim Acta,* Vol. 16, 1960, p. 58.
[2] Lippincott, E. R., Whatley, L. S., and Duecker, H. C., in *Applied Infrared Spectroscopy,* D. N. Kendall, Ed., Reinhold, New York, 1966.
[3] McCrone, W. C., Draftz, R. G., and Delly, J. C., *The Particle Atlas,* Ann Arbor Science Publishers, Inc., Ann Arbor, MI, 1967.
[4] Joseph, M. L., *Introductory Textile Science,* Holt, Rinehart and Winston, New York, 1977.

Edward G. Bartick[1]

Considerations for Fiber Sampling with Infrared Microspectroscopy

REFERENCE: Bartick, E. G., **"Considerations for Fiber Sampling with Infrared Microspec-troscopy,"** *The Design, Sample Handling, and Applications of Infrared Microscopes, ASTM STP 949*, P. B. Roush, Ed., American Society for Testing and Materials, Philadelphia, 1987, pp. 64–73.

ABSTRACT: The sampling of fibers by infrared microspectroscopy is considered. Fibers are grouped into three categories: 30 to 50 μm diameter, less than 30 μm diameter, and small clumps of fibers. In the first type, rapid analysis can be easily accomplished without any preparation; however, the effects of the circular cross section of the fibers must be considered. In the second type, the best results are obtained by flattening the fibers. In the third type, the most reproducible results are acquired by pressing the clump into a potassium bromide substrate. When doing spectral subtraction, all categories require that the mixture and the subtracted spectra are obtained under the same sampling conditions. When applying these considerations to the analysis of fibers, microscopy combined with infrared (IR) spectroscopy should prove to be a very viable analytical method.

KEY WORDS: infrared spectroscopy, infrared microspectroscopy, fiber analysis

In the early work of combining microscopy with infrared (IR) spectroscopy, workers were able to obtain spectra on specimens between 10 and 20 μm in diameter. Microscopes have proven very useful as a convenient means of sampling routine size specimens as well [1]. Very simple techniques have been devised for specimen handling of both micro and routine sizes. Good qualitative spectra are frequently obtained. This capability has certainly sparked a great deal of interest in the analytical community.

However, as other papers in this volume describe, there are specimen handling aspects which must be considered for the successful application of microscopy to infrared spectroscopic analysis. Various approaches have been described in these papers. This author will describe the approaches that he has taken.

Techniques specifically developed for and applicable to sampling fiber specimens will be described. Fiber analysis by infrared spectroscopy is important in the textile and paper industries. Infrared (IR) spectroscopy of fibers is also necessary in the areas of forensic science and industrial contaminant analysis. In these fields, the value of applying IR microspectroscopy to fiber analysis is rapidly becoming recognized.

Fibers of three general types are considered. The first class of fibers is between 30 and 50 μm in diameter. Next, fibers less than 30 μm in diameter are considered. Third, small clumps of fibers are analyzed. An additional fiber category of greater than 50 μm in diameter has previously been considered [2].

[1] Research chemist, Spectra-Tech, Inc., 652 Glenbrook Rd., Stamford, CT 06906. Current address: Forensic Science Research and Training Center, FBI Academy, Quantico, VA 22135.

Experimental

The microscope used in this work was a Spectra-Scope™ manufactured by Spectra-Tech, Inc. This microscope fits in the sample compartment and utilizes the detector of the spectrometer. A Nicolet 20SXB FT-IR spectrometer with a narrowband mercury cadmium telluride (MCT) detector was employed. A resolution of 4 cm^{-1} was used with Happ-Ganzel apodization. Scan times varied between specimens and are listed in the text.

Discussion and Results

Fibers Between 30 and 50 μm in Diameter

With MCT detectors, spectra of single fibers approximately 30 to 50 μm in diameter can be readily obtained in the order of one minute. Little specimen preparation is required other than taping the fiber tightly across a holder and positioning the fiber in the beam. Rectangular apertures are best used to mask out stray light. They provide a much greater sampling area than circular apertures when studying single fibers. Fibers should always be positioned in the same direction to avoid variations in the spectra due to molecular orientation conditions caused by drawing the fibers in the production process. Figure 1 displays the spectrum of a poly(acrylonitrile-co-ethyl acrylate) fiber (Orlon) approximately 40 μm in diameter obtained in the above fashion. The spectrum has a good signal-to-noise ratio and the peak frequencies match reference spectra. However, the ratios of the less intense bands to the stronger bands are considerably greater than in the reference spectra. This condition results from the circular cross section of the fiber which produces a variable pathlength. This

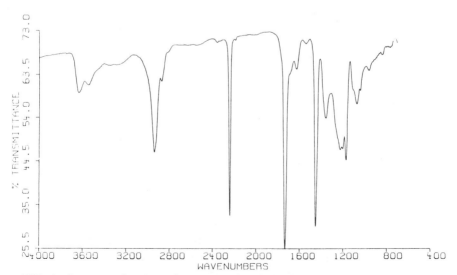

FIG. 1—*Spectrum of a 40-μm-diameter poly(acrylonitrile-co-ethyl acrylate) fiber (Orlon) with no preparation except for straightening and taping across the holder.*

condition has been described by Messerschmidt [3]. Hirschfeld has described a similar situation when using variable pathlength cells [4]. This effect increases the range of the fiber thicknesses from which we can obtain spectra without peaks totally "bottoming out." Qualitative interpretation is still readily accomplished. No problem is encountered unless one is interested in making computerized difference comparisons between circular fibers and spectra obtained on flat materials. The compared spectra need be obtained under the same conditions. To do so, the fibers need to be flattened.

Fibers can be flattened by several means. Fibers for this work were flattened using a pressure anvil cell previously described [2]. The cell utilizes modified holders for a "Handi-Press," originally designed for preparing potassium bromide (KBr) pellets. The cell flattens a fiber by placing it between polished metal anvils. The fiber is positioned by placing it in a two-ply paper holder with a small hole in the center. The fiber is placed across the hole between the plies and held in place with pressure-sensitive adhesive. The cell has been described as a means of flattening specimens that are optically too dense to obtain good spectra. Fibers greater than 50 μm often fall in this category. However, for fibers less than 50 μm, the ability to increase the sampling area is also advantageous because of the improved signal-to-noise ratio and the reduced diffraction effects [3]. The photomicrograph shown in Fig. 2, taken through the IR microscope, illustrates the considerably increased area of the flattened portion of the fiber. The diameter was increased from approximately 40 to 230 μm. The spectra in Fig. 3 show a comparison in absorbance between spectra of a flattened lower and nonflattened fiber upper. With the exception of the size of the apertured field, the

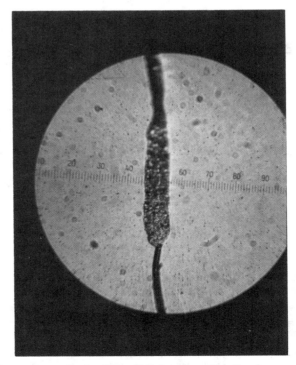

FIG. 2—*Photomicrograph of a flattened Orlon fiber. The diameter was increased from approximately 40 to 230 μm.*

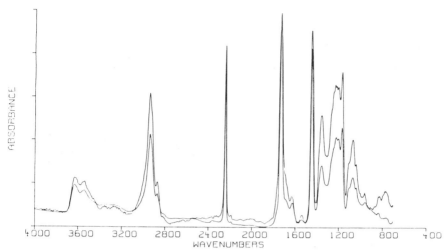

FIG. 3—Upper, *spectrum of a nonflattened Orlon fiber.* Lower, *spectrum of a flattened Orlon fiber.*

instrumental conditions were the same in both cases. Note the improved signal-to-noise ratio and the difference in peak intensity ratios between the spectra. It is also important to note that changes in chemical structure can be induced by pressure in the flattening process. It has not appeared to present a problem in the spectra presented here. However, it is important to be aware of the possibility and to look out for changes in band intensities and shapes.

Fibers Less than 30 µm in Diameter

When the diameter of fibers is less than 30 µm, sampling becomes less than routine. Longer scan times are required because of the reduced energy and more severe diffraction effects become obvious. Figure 4 shows a spectrum of a polyethylene teraphthalate (PET) fiber approximately 13 µm in diameter which was image-apertured to approximately 7 µm. While the specimen was scanned longer than previous fibers, 1000 times (approximately 8 min), considerable degradation of the signal-to-noise ratio is obvious. The C-O stretching bands near 1250 and 1000 cm^{-1} are less intense than are obtained with films. This is a result of diffraction effects which produce stray light causing a reduction of the intensities of bands at the longer wavelengths. When using the "Handi-Anvil" cell technique of flattening the specimen, the diameter was increased to approximately 54 µm and then was image-masked to approximately 36 µm. The improved signal-to-noise ratio is apparent when scanning for only 128 scans (approximately 1 min) as displayed in Fig. 5. However, the reduced band intensities are still evident when comparing the single-fiber spectrum with that of a pressed film from a group of fibers. Figure 6 compares the spectrum in absorbance of the flattened single fiber with that of a pressed film produced from a group of fibers. The C-O stretching bands are greater in intensity for the film and the carbonyl band is less intense compared to the single-fiber spectrum. This may be difficult to observe on the overlayed spectra, because of the crossover of the carbonyl peaks. The variation of the band intensities could become a problem when doing spectral subtraction. If the image of the flattened fiber is

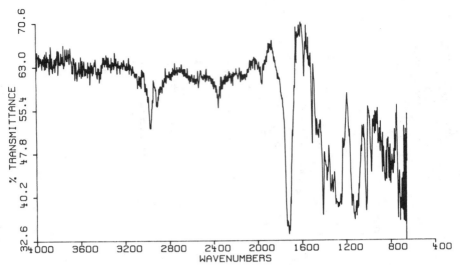

FIG. 4—*Spectrum of a polyethylene teraphthalate fiber (PET) approximately 13 μm in diameter taped across the holder (1000 scans).*

masked to a greater extent, less diffraction takes place at a sacrifice of the signal-to-noise ratio. Spectra obtained by masking the image to 36 versus 13 μm were compared. Very little difference was observed when overlaying the spectra. However, when performing spectral subtraction, residuals are noticeable which result from variations in band intensities (Fig. 7). Figure 8 shows the difference after subtracting the spectrum of the 13-μm versus a 17-μm apertured specimen. Less residual is observed in this case. Therefore, when doing difference spectroscopy with these types of fibers or with microspecimens in general, it is

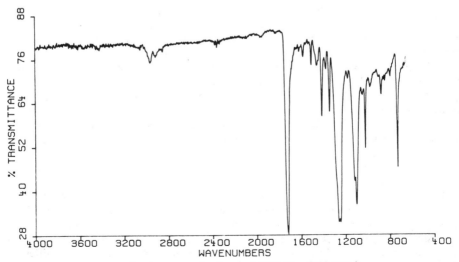

FIG. 5—*Spectrum of a flattened PET fiber (128 scans).*

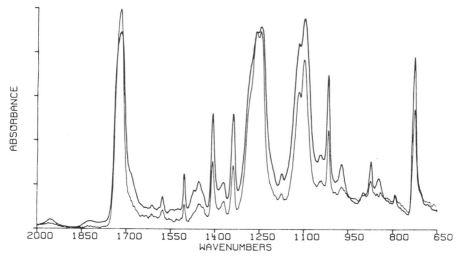

FIG. 6—*Comparison of a single flattened fiber and a group of PET fibers flattened into a film. A reversal of the C-O and the C = O bands relative band intensities takes place between the spectra.*

important to aperture the specimen similarly in each case in order to keep diffraction effects more equal.

Small Clumps of Fibers

Spectra can frequently be obtained from clumps of fibers by locating an adequate density of fibers in the beam while viewing [1]. This technique can be useful as either a microtech-

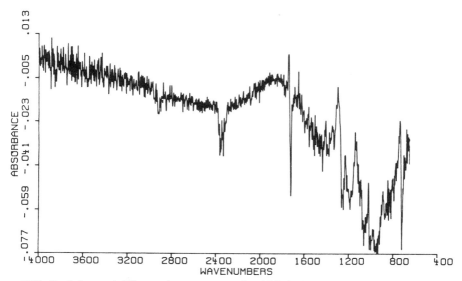

FIG. 7—*Subtracted difference between spectra in which the image was apertured to 36 and to 13 μm on a flattened PET fiber.*

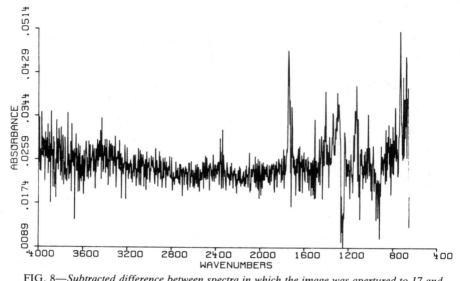

FIG. 8—*Subtracted difference between spectra in which the image was apertured to 17 and to 13 μm on a flattened PET fiber.*

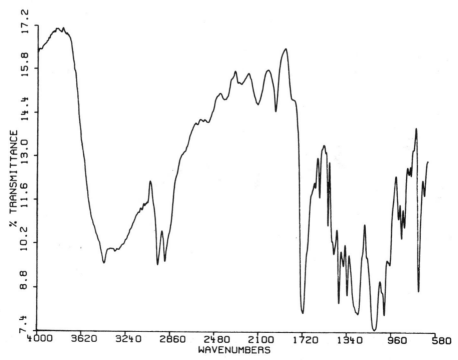

FIG. 9—*Spectrum of cotton-polyester prepared by pressing a small clump into a KBr substrate.*

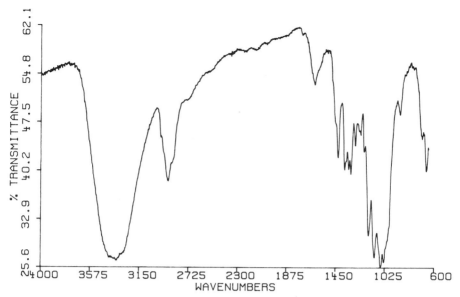

FIG. 10—*Spectrum of cotton prepared as in Fig. 10.*

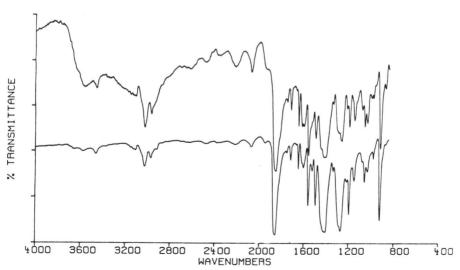

FIG. 11—Upper spectrum: *subtracted difference between spectra in Figs. 10 and 11.* Lower spectrum: *polyester prepared as in Fig. 10.*

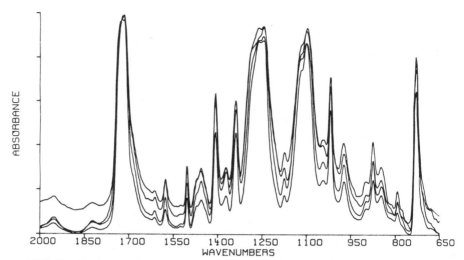

FIG. 12—*Comparison between spectra of four PET fiber clumps separately prepared as in Figs. 10, 11, and 12.*

nique or for larger amounts of specimen. However, when spectral subtraction is desired, problems arise. Stray light and uncontrolled variation in band intensity ratios make good subtractions unlikely. The fiber clumps can be compacted to remove, or at least reduce these conditions. This can be accomplished with use of the Handi-Anvil technique, combined with a KBr substrate [2]. KBr substrates can be prepared from paper holders with 2- or 3-mm holes in the center. Powdered KBr is placed in the hole and pressed. Once prepared, a small fiber clump is located on the surface of the substrate, placed in the press and squeezed. The fibers do not flatten out, but become embedded into the KBr. Very repeatable spectra can be prepared in this way. This technique is particularly useful when blends are suspected. Figure 9 shows a spectrum of a cotton-polyester blend obtained in this way. If a component of the blend is known, it can be subtracted out. Figure 10 shows a spectrum of cotton obtained in this fashion. This spectrum was subtracted from the blend, producing the upper spectrum in Fig. 11. The lower spectrum of PET fibers was obtained separately. The spectra compare reasonably well with the exception of the OH stretching region near 3600 cm⁻¹. This is likely to be due to a greater amount of water adsorption in the blend specimen.

In the interest of determining the amount of repeatability obtainable with this technique, four separate specimens of PET fibers were prepared. The spectra were full-scale plotted and overlayed as shown in Fig. 12. Qualitatively these spectra compare very well. However, minor variations can be observed in peak shapes and relative intensities. These possibly result from variation of orientation of the individual fibers in the clumps. Pressure effects are less likely to occur, because the fibers become embedded into the KBr. Several PET spectra were subtracted from one another. Some subtracted very well, while with others significant residuals remained. Therefore, caution must be applied when performing subtractions of spectra with specimens prepared by this technique.

Conclusion

Specimen handling techniques for several categories of fibers have been described. When performing infrared microspectroscopic analysis on these types of specimens, we must consider the diameter and the quantity of the specimens. This is necessary in order to determine the type of preparation which will best suit the situation. When the various sampling effects are understood, qualitative interpretation of the spectra can readily be made. However, when performing spectral subtraction, much greater care must be taken to assure the sampling conditions for the reference and specimen spectra. With the application of the techniques described, infrared microspectroscopy with microscope accessories is expected to prove itself as a very powerful tool for fiber analysis.

References

[1] Bartick, E. G., *Applied Spectroscopy*, Vol. 39, No. 5, Sept./Oct. 1985, pp. 885–889.
[2] Bartick, E. G. in *Proceedings*, SPIE International Conference on Fourier and Computerized Infrared Spectroscopy, Society of Photo-Optical Engineers, Bellingham, WA, Vol. 553, 1985, pp. 322–323.
[3] Messerschmidt, R. G., in this publication, pp. 12–26.
[4] Hirschfeld, T., *Applied Spectroscopy*, Vol. 39, No. 3, May/June 1985, pp. 424–430.

Francis M. Mirabella, Jr.[1]

Applications of Microscopic Fourier Transform Infrared Spectrophotometry Sampling Techniques for the Analysis of Polymer Systems

REFERENCE: Mirabella, F. M., Jr., "**Applications of Microscopic Fourier Transform Infrared Spectrophotometry Sampling Techniques for the Analysis of Polymer Systems,**" *The Design, Sample Handling, and Applications of Infrared Microscopes, ASTM STP 949,* P. B. Roush, Ed., American Society for Testing and Materials, Philadelphia, 1987, pp. 74–83.

ABSTRACT: The packaging industry is in the midst of a revolution in which plastics are replacing other materials. The form of such plastic packaging is often complex multilayer films. Analytical techniques are described for the characterization of such multilayer structures. These techniques include internal reflection spectroscopy and microsampling/Fourier transform infrared spectrophotometry (FT-IR). The composition of polymeric films is shown to be amenable to characterization by these techniques.

A technique to simultaneously measure thermal property response and infrared spectra on specimens of microscopic dimensions has been demonstrated. The apparatus consists of a microscopic differential scanning calorimetric cell and infrared microsampling accessory mounted in a FT-IR. The technique was demonstrated through the study of the melting of polypropylene. The technique is expected to have a wide range of applications in many areas of science, including chemistry, physics, and biology.

KEY WORDS: infrared microspectroscopy, thermal analysis

The use of plastics in the form of a single-layer structure is common in the packaging industry. However, the use of complex multilayer structures which offer vastly improved performance over single-layer structures has increased dramatically due to the advancement of the technology for manufacturing such structures. Figure 1 shows the position and function of some polymers in multilayer film structures.

Coextrusions of three and five layers are common and those up to about ten layers are currently found in the marketplace. These complex structures, which may be designed with a combination of desired properties such as oxygen barrier and strength, can be manufactured at nearly the same cost as single-ply film, due to the major advances made in coextrusion technology. An alternative method to multilayer film production is lamination of single-ply films to form a multilayer structure. Further, coextruded multilayer structures can be laminated to form a more complex structure.

This explosive growth in the use of multilayer films has presented a challenge to characterize these structures. It is often necessary to identify the layers, determine the layer thicknesses, quantitatively determine the layer composition and additives therein, and de-

---

[1] Research associate, Norchem, Inc., Rolling Meadows, IL 60008.

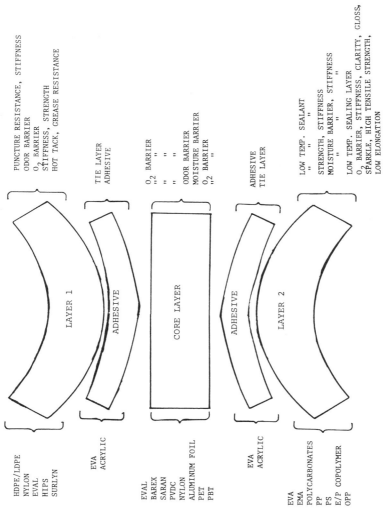

FIG. 1—*Position and function of materials in typical multilayer films.*

termine orientation in the layers. The first part of this paper presents recent advances in the characterization of multilayer structures; the second part describes a new technique employing simultaneous differential scanning calorimetry and infrared microspectroscopy for the study of polymers.

The characterization of the current generation of multilayer films has been found to require a number of techniques applied in series or simultaneously because of the complexity of these systems. It is typically not possible to simply separate the layers and analyze them individually since the layers are usually securely adhered to one another. The problems of qualitatively and quantitatively defining such a structure are formidable.

In essentially all cases, the most obvious first step is to visually observe the specimen in an optical microscope. It is necessary to microtome a thin cross section at right angles to the surface of the film in order to prepare the specimen so that the individual layers can be conveniently observed with the optical microscope. The microtomed section can then be viewed in the microscope and the various layers and interfaces between layers may be observed if sufficient contrast between layers can be achieved.

If the layer structure of a multilayer film has been investigated by optical microscopy and been partially or completely defined as to number of layers and layer thicknesses, the next logical step is often to record the transmission infrared spectrum through the entire film. This yields a composite spectrum of all the layers with intensities related both to the layer thicknesses and the absorptivity of the various materials in the layers. The composite spectrum can be quite complex, depending on the number of different materials present in the multilayer film. However, with the use of digital spectral subtraction and with a knowledge of the appearance of the layers from microscopy, it is often possible to identify some or all of the materials in the layers. This becomes more difficult as the number of layers increases and as the film thickness decreases. This method of digitally subtracting each layer in sequence is sometimes referred to as "spectral stripping" and is the analog of physical separation of layers.

Internal Reflection Spectroscopy

Internal reflection spectroscopy (IRS), also known as attenuated total reflection spectroscopy (ATR), is extremely useful for examining the outermost layers of multilayer films. Basically, the IRS technique consists of pressing the specimen surface against a higher index of refraction crystal, passing the infrared radiation through this crystal, and recording the spectrum of the specimen surface in contact with the crystal.

Microscopic Infrared Spectroscopy

A powerful method to map specimen areas, that is, identify various portions of the specimen, and to analyze multilayer films with infrared spectroscopy down to diameters of approximately 10 μm has recently become available. This method utilizes an optical microscope to locate and view small areas of a specimen. The areas may then be photographed and measurements made to determine the size of the areas. This microscope mounts into a Fourier transform infrared (FT-IR) spectrometer. The FT-IR microsampling accessory used is available from Digilab, Cambridge, Maine. Subsequently the infrared spectrum of the specific area of interest may be recorded. A schematic diagram of an instrument which is capable of performing these tasks is shown in Fig. 2. This microscope accessory is very useful for locating and then identifying small inhomogeneities, such as a particle or oxidized zone in a plastic film. Its use is unique for the identification of the layers in a multilayer film. In order to analyze a multilayer film with this FT-IR microsampling accessory, the

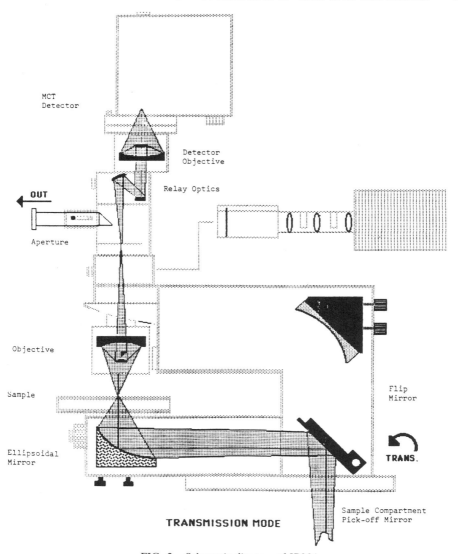

MCT
Detector

Detector
Objective

Relay Optics

OUT

Aperture

Objective

Sample

Ellipsoidal
Mirror

Flip
Mirror

TRANS.

TRANSMISSION MODE

Sample Compartment
Pick-off Mirror

FIG. 2—*Schematic diagram of IRMA.*

multilayer film is turned on edge and a thin (25 to 50 μm) cross section is microtomed from the edge. Microtomy was performed at ambient temperature on a Reichert sliding microtome with steel knife (Profile C). The infrared spectrum of each layer is then obtained by focusing the infrared radiation on a small area (10 by 10 μm or larger) of each layer. The infrared spectrum may be obtained either by transmission or reflection modes. The infrared spectra of each layer can, in the ideal case, be obtained separately and the layers identified. However, in cases where layers are very thin (less than 20 μm) the infrared spectra contain information from more than one layer. The thickness dimension and position of each layer from the optical microscope, along with infrared spectra of the layers, can typically permit the complete identification of the layer structure. An analysis of a multilayer film of structure similar to the film in Fig. 1 was performed with this technique. The infrared spectra of Layer 1 the core layer, and Layer 2 in Fig. 1 were obtained as shown in Fig. 3. Spectra were identified by computer spectral search. Since the spectra were reasonably free of distortions, computer search routines were successful in identifying the component layers. Layer 1 was found to be polypropylene with reground film containing poly(ethylene-vinyl alcohol) (EVAL®). The core layer was EVAL®. Layer 2 was polypropylene. The adhesive layers shown in Fig. 1 are typically very thin (10 μm or less) and cannot be identified from the spectra in Fig. 3. Careful, sequential mapping of infrared spectra across the cross section of the microtomed film section yields a large number of spectra in a typical analysis of this kind. Using this approach, the infrared spectra can then be compared with the optical microscopic photographs of the same section and a thorough identification of each layer can be made. The adhesive layers can then be identified, usually as poly(ethylene-vinyl alcohol) (EVA), an acrylate, or a modified polyolefin such as maleic anhydride grafted polyethylene.

Application of Microscopic FT-IR: Simultaneous Differential Scanning Calorimetry and FT-IR

Introduction

The capability to simultaneously measure thermal property response and infrared spectra on specimens of microscopic dimensions can provide important insight into structural changes associated with thermal response for a wide range of systems. The simultaneous measurement of the thermal response in a differential scanning calorimeter (DSC) and the infrared spectra in an FT-IR can provide this capability. In particular, the use of a DSC cell adapted for microscopic observation during thermal treatment combined with an infrared microsampling accessory (IRMA) in an FT-IR permits the collection of such data simultaneously. The range of applications of such a technique is undoubtedly immense. The various phase transitions and thermal responses of crystalline and amorphous polymers, polymer blends and copolymers, liquid crystalline polymers, as well as small molecules could be correlated with the structural information derivable from the simultaneously collected infrared spectra. This would permit studies of reaction and crystallization kinetics, oxidation, efficacy of additives, etc. It is often convenient to be able to perform such studies on rather small specimens. In many other cases, only very small quantities of material are available for study. This presents no particular problem for the simultaneous DSC/microscopic FT-IR technique.

Experimental Apparatus

The infrared spectrophotometer used was a Nicolet 6000 FT-IR. All spectra were recorded at 4 cm^{-1} resolution. Acceptable S/N was obtained by coadding 100 spectra at a mirror velocity of 0.586 cm/s. A Digilab transmittance IRMA with 250-μm MCT detector was used to focus the infrared radiation through the DSC cell. The DSC cell used was a Mettler FP84 thermal analysis microscopy cell. A Mettler FP80 central processor with recorder was used to control the temperature in the FP84 DSC cell. Typical DSC thermograms and infrared spectra could be simultaneously recorded with this combined apparatus. A schematic diagram of the DSC microscopy cell is shown in Fig. 4. The DSC microscopy cell was placed on the stage of the IRMA. The infrared beam was required to pass through a 2.5-mm hole in the bottom of the DSC cell, travel 3.0 mm (thereby passing through the specimen and specimen cup) and exit from the DSC cell through a 3.0-mm hole on the way to the MCT detector. Thus, the infrared beam must pass through a cylinder of 2.5 mm diameter and 3.0 mm length. This requires a rather demanding alignment procedure prior to operation. In order

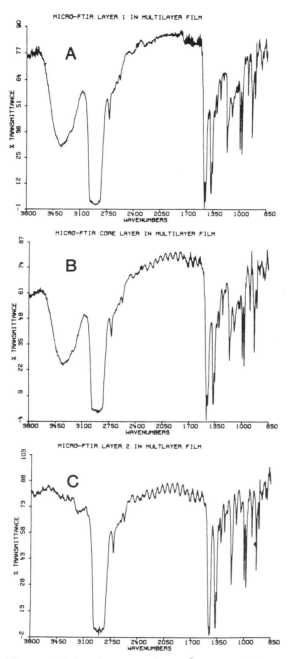

FIG. 3—(A) *Microscopic infrared spectrum of Layer 1 in Fig. 1;* (B) *Microscopic infrared spectrum of core layer in Fig. 1;* (C) *Microscopic infrared spectrum of Layer 2 in Fig. 1.*

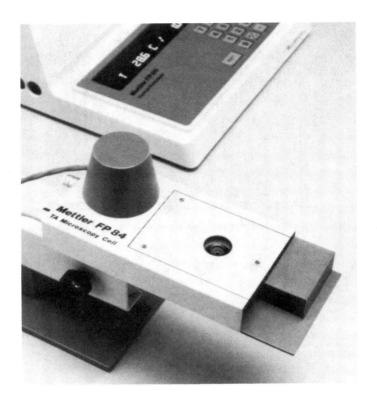

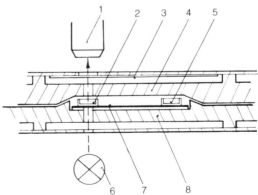

1 Microscope objective
2 Sapphire sample crucible
3 Heat protection filter
4 Metal plate with heating wires
5 Sapphire reference crucible

6 Microscope light source
7 DSC measuring sensor
8 Metal plate with heating wires
 and Pt100 resistance sensor

FIG. 4—*Photograph and schematic diagram of microscopy/DSC cell.*

to permit both microscopical observation and transmission infrared spectroscopy of the specimen, speciman cups of sodium chloride (NaCl) were used to hold the specimen. For simultaneous optical microscopy and DSC, sapphire specimen cups are used. The thermal conductivity of NaCl is 1.3 g cal/s cm °C, that of sapphire is 0.6 g cal/s cm °C, while that of aluminum is 55.9 g cal/s cm °C, all at 100°C. Thus, NaCl is a reasonably good conductor of heat, but it is also transparent to visible light and infrared radiation in the wavelength range of 0.35 to 15 μm. It is therefore an excellent material for use in the present application.

The combination of temperature program rates in the DSC and spectral collection rates in the FT-IR offers a vast range in which to collect data simultaneously. Of course, the FT-IR has the capability to rapidly collect spectra over the entire DSC thermogram. The collection of spectra at the rate of about one per second, thereby, results in the accumulation of a large number of spectra over a 15 to 30 min DSC experiment. These spectra may be important for fully elucidating the thermal response under investigation. For the purposes of this work and for ease of presentation, fewer spectra, collected over longer time, will be presented. For the purposes of this work, the DSC was programmed at 10°C/min. The FT-IR collected 100 scans in 1 min at the aforementioned conditions. The lower-temperature spectra, remote from the melting endotherm, were collected over a 10°C temperature interval. The higher-temperature spectra, in the vicinity of the melting endotherm, were collected isothermally. This was accomplished with the manual program controller of the Mettler FP80 DSC controller. This device permitted the program to be halted and the temperature to be held to ±0.1°C at will. The program could then be restarted when the infrared spectra had been collected at a particular temperature.

Demonstration of Simultaneous (DSC/FT-IR)

The particular application to which the simultaneous microscopic DSC and FT-IR technique was put first was the study of polymer melting. Thermal analysis of polymers is a useful technique for obtaining qualitative information, for example, for determining the type of polymer. In some cases, however, the thermal analysis technique is, by its nature, not well suited for quantitative analysis because polymers do not have well-defined melting points or heats of fusion. This is because real polymer crystals are virtually never in ther-

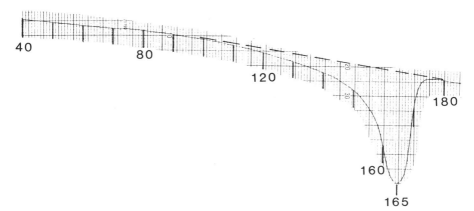

FIG. 5—*DSC thermogram of polypropylene which was previously slowly cooled from the melt over 5½ h. Program rate was 10°C/min.*

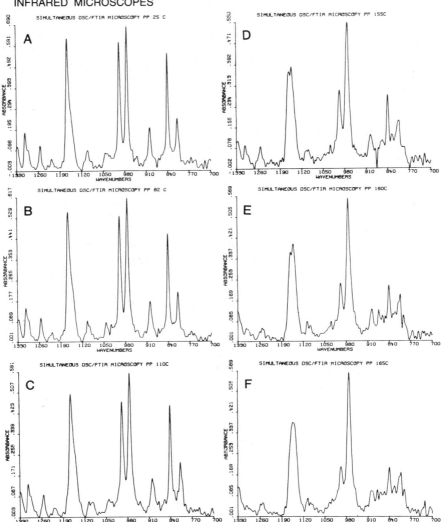

FIG. 6—*Selected infrared spectra taken over DSC thermogram in Fig. 5. Spectra were taken as follows:* (A) *25°C isothermal;* (B) *82°C collected over 72 to 82°C temperature interval;* (C) *110°C collected over 100 to 110°C temperature interval;* (D) *155°C isothermal;* (E) *160°C isothermal;* (F) *165°C isothermal.*

modynamic equilibrium but rather are formed on the basis of kinetic factors during crys tallization. For this reason, polymer crystals may exhibit a large range of melting temper atures and heats of fusion. This is due to the thickness and perfection of crystal lamellae produced under the kinetic conditions of crystallization. These facts compromise the quan titative value of thermal analysis data and, further, may inhibit the use of such data for qualitative purposes since different polymers may exhibit similar melting endotherms when subjected to particular thermal histories. Typically, the above considerations are realized and thermal analysis is quite useful in spite of these limitations. However, this situation may be significantly improved by the simultaneous recording of the DSC thermogram and the corresponding infrared spectra as a function of temperature.

The melting of polypropylene is a particularly interesting case, due to the drastic changes in the infrared spectrum as this transition occurs. The changes in the infrared spectrum have been explained on the basis of particular bands arising from a particular phase, crystalline or noncrystalline [1], or on the basis of particular bands arising from a critical minimum number of monomer units arranged helically and necessary for observation of the band [2,3]. The melting of a 1-mg specimen of polypropylene that had previously been slowly cooled from the melt over a 5½-h period was studied by the simultaneous microscopic DSC and FT-IR.

The DSC thermogram is shown in Fig. 5 and some of the infrared spectra collected over this temperature range are shown in Fig. 6. Changes in the infrared spectra can be first observed in the 110°C spectrum. This spectrum was taken over the temperature interval from 100 to 110°C. These changes correspond with the first evidence of heat uptake observed in the DSC thermogram in Fig. 5. Large changes in the infrared spectra can be observed in Fig. 6 as the melting endotherm is transversed. Careful study of the thermogram and infrared spectra using the simultaneous microscopic DSC and FT-IR technique may aid in the explanation of the structural changes that occur in polypropylene during melting. A detailed analysis of the infrared spectra and correlation with the melting endotherm of polypropylene is beyond the scope of this paper. However, the disappearance, frequency shift, or profile change of the spectral bands may be correlated with the bond assignments for polypropylene [4], thus enabling correlation of the thermally induced changes in the infrared spectra with effects on particular chemical bonds.

Conclusions

Techniques have been demonstrated to characterize the layers in complex multilayer plastic films. The outer layers were shown to be amenable to characterization by internal reflection spectroscopy. The individual layers were shown to be amenable to characterization by combined optical microscopy and infrared microspectroscopy.

A technique has been demonstrated to simultaneously study the thermal response and infrared spectral changes of specimens of microscopic dimensions. This technique is expected to have a wide range of applications in many areas of science, including chemistry, physics, and biology. Further studies of polymer, as well as other systems, are in progress.

References

[1] Samuels, R. J., *Makromolekulare Chemie, Supplement,* Vol. 4, 1981, p. 241.
[2] Kissin, Yu. V. and Rishina, L., *European Polymer Journal,* Vol. 12, 1976, p. 757.
[3] Glotin, M., Rahalkar, R. R., Hendra, P. J., Cudby, M. E. A., and Willis, H. S., *Polymer,* Vol. 22, 1981, p. 731.
[4] Miyazawa, T., *Journal of Polymer Science: Part C, Polymer Symposia,* Vol. 7, 1964, p. 59.

Matthew A. Harthcock[1]

Applications of Recent Developments in Fourier Transform Infrared Spectroscopic Microsampling Techniques to Polymeric Materials

REFERENCE: Harthcock, M. A., **"Applications of Recent Developments in Fourier Transform Infrared Spectroscopic Microsampling Techniques to Polymeric Materials,"** *The Design, Sample Handling, and Applications of Infrared Microscopes, ASTM STP 949,* P. B. Roush, Ed., American Society for Testing and Materials, Philadelphia, 1987, pp. 84–96.

ABSTRACT: Infrared microspectroscopy utilizing an optical microscope coupled with appropriate optics for recording infrared spectra has two advantages over "standard" microsampling techniques: (1) elimination or reduced time for specimen preparation and (2) infrared spectra can be recorded on specific microscopic regions of a specimen. Applications of the technique to polymeric materials are presented to demonstrate its advantages and its value as an analytical tool in the field of polymer science. Examples include (1) identification of gels or inclusions in a polyethylene film, (2) molecular structure differences due to branching in a bimodal morphology of spherulite sizes in an ethylene/olefin copolymer, (3) comparison of attenuated total reflectance and microtransmittance data obtained for polymer laminates, and (4) the identification of the composition of a "streaked" area in a polymer film which coats the surface of some aluminum foil.

KEY WORDS: infrared spectroscopy, Fourier transform infrared spectroscopy (FT-IR), microsampling, microspectroscopy, polymers, gels, morphology, laminates

The concept of infrared microspectroscopy using an optical microscope for aligning and viewing microscopic specimens was reported several years ago (for example, see Ref *1*). However, the utility of the technique has not been fully exploited until recently and is due to improvements in Fourier transform infrared spectroscopy (FT-IR). High-sensitivity detectors (for example, liquid nitrogen-cooled MCT detectors), efficient/high throughput optics of the interferometer based spectrophotometers and high-intensity infrared sources have brought about a renaissance in infrared microsampling [2–7].

The addition of an optical microscope modified appropriately allows the visible light (viewing) path and infrared radiation path to be colinear resulting in two advantages of the technique over "standard" microsampling techniques. (Here "standard" microsampling techniques refer to those microsampling techniques that do not use an optical microscope coupled with the infrared optics.) The two advantages are: (1) time-consuming and difficult specimen preparation associated with "standard" microsampling is eliminated or greatly reduced and (2) infrared spectra can be recorded on very specific regions of a specimen. These advantages will become obvious from the examples presented in this paper.

[1] Project leader, Analytical and Engineering Sciences, B-1218, Texas Applied Science and Technology Laboratories, Dow Chemical U.S.A., Freeport, TX 77541.

Commercially available infrared/microscope accessories are available to record absorbance or various reflectance (for example, specular reflectance or reflectance/absorption) infrared spectra. The versatility in the types of infrared spectra that can be recorded allows wide applicability of the technique. This is particularly the case for polymeric materials. Reported here are applications of infrared microspectroscopy as an analytical tool to solve problems involving polymeric materials and to understand fundamental questions in polymer science.

Experimental

Infrared Instrumentation

The infrared spectra reported were recorded on a Bio-Rad Laboratories, Digilab Division FTS-50 Fourier transform infrared spectrophotometer equipped with a potassium bromide (KBr) beamsplitter and liquid nitrogen-cooled, narrowband MCT detector. A Digilab universal infrared microscope accessory (both transmittance and reflectance capabilities) was used for all of the microsampling. A rectangular aperture was used to aperture or mask the region for which the infrared spectrum was desired. Background spectra were recorded in each case through the same size aperture and polarizer position as that through which the specimen spectra were recorded.

The attenuated total reflectance (ATR) spectra were collected on a Nicolet 60SX Fourier transform infrared spectrophotometer using a Nicolet Micro ATR accessory (4X beam condenser) and a narrowband MCT detector. A KRS-5 parallelogram prism (45°) with dimensions of 25 by 10 by 3 mm was used.

Specimen Viewing

In order to isolate specific regions of a specimen, the specimen must be viewed. Our laboratory has expanded the viewing capabilities of our microscope accessory beyond that of the illuminator that allows normal incident reflected light to be used to view the surface of a specimen. A fiber optics illumination system is used to allow viewing the specimen with transmitted visible light and reflected light from side illumination. Also, polarization filters for the eyepiece (analyzer) and illumination system (polarizer) are used to view the specimen and the microscope has been modified appropriately to allow viewing of the specimen with polarized light. A salt window "sandwiching" technique is also sometimes used to provide improved contrast between various morphological features of a specimen. The technique is analogous to the optical microscopy technique of placing a specimen between two plates with an immersion oil. In this case, the plates are infrared transparent salt windows and, if necessary or desired, an infrared solvent is used for the immersion oil.

Specimen Preparation

Some of the specimens studied required no preparation because the materials are self-supporting (gels and film on aluminum foil) while others required microtoming (polyethylene morphology and laminates). The microtoming was done using a Sorvall MT-6000 microtome equipped with an FS-1000 cryosectioning chamber. The laminates or multilayer structures were embedded in an epoxy resin matrix which was cured and then cooled to $-30°C$ using liquid nitrogen for cross sectioning. The polyethylene specimen was cross sectioned by cooling to $-30°C$ with liquid nitrogen. The samples were prepared using a glass knife.

Optical Micrographs

The optical micrographs were taken on the same or similar sections of the specimens used for the infrared analysis. A Reichert optical microscope was used.

Results and Discussion

Heterogeneous Polymeric Materials

Infrared microspectroscopy allows the identification of individual particles or regions in a heterogeneous polymeric material. The technique allows the specimen to be viewed and specific regions (or particles) of the specimen can be isolated using the aperture and the infrared spectra recorded. This demonstrates both advantages of the technique-reduction in specimen preparation and the specificity of the technique. For example, previously reported [7] was the use of the technique to isolate individual particles in a two particle system. "Standard" microsampling techniques would result in an infrared spectrum showing characteristic absorptions of both particles or would have required the particles to be separated under a microscope before preparing the specimens and recording the infrared spectra. In this report, examples of the technique's utility in investigating gels or inclusions in a polymer film and a heterogeneous morphology in a ethylene/olefin copolymer will be presented.

Figure 1 shows the optical micrograph of a gel or inclusion in a polyethylene film. The gel is approximately 250 μm in diameter. Gels or inclusions in films are studied using the transmittance capabilities of the technique. Gels smaller than this (30 to 75 μm) have been also studied successfully in our laboratory using the technique. Figure 2 presents the infrared spectra obtained for the gel and the bulk polyethylene film surrounding the gel. The spectrum of the gel shows characteristic absorption bands of polyethylene but absorption bands due to acid dimers and acid salt structures are also observed in the spectrum. The gel was thus determined to be composed of a foreign material believed to originate from an ethylene/acid type copolymer.

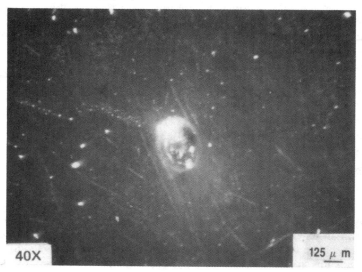

40X   125 μ m

FIG. 1—*Optical micrograph of gel or inclusion in polyethylene film (×40 magnification).*

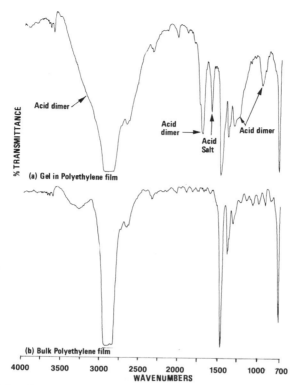

FIG. 2—*Infrared microtransmittance spectra between 4000 and 700 cm⁻¹ of (a) gel in polyethylene film and (b) bulk polyethylene film. (Collection conditions for the two spectra: 8 cm⁻¹ resolution, 64 scans, 150 by 150 μm aperture.)*

The next example is the use of the technique to record infrared spectra on specific regions of an ethylene/olefin copolymer exhibiting a heterogeneous or bimodal morphology. Before discussing the specifics of this example, a brief discussion of the experimental details for recording the infrared spectra will be given.

The heterogeneous or bimodal morphology in the ethylene/olefin copolymer was observed using polarized transmitted visible light as regions containing large spherulites and adjacent regions containing small spherulites. Optical micrographs showing this morphology are presented in Fig. 3 at different magnifications. Approximately 50 by 50 μm regions were apertured containing either the large or small spherulites using polarized visible light. The cross sectional thickness or infrared specimen pathlength was found to be approximately 15 μm from the interference fringes in the infrared spectrum [8]. However, these interference fringes caused a problem when interested in the weaker absorption bands due to the amorphous phase in the 1250 to 1400 cm⁻¹ region. As a result, an infrared wire grid polarizer was placed after the specimen in order to minimize the interference fringes observed in the resulting infrared spectra [9]. Figure 4 gives a description and views of the infrared polarizer attached to the Cassegrainian objective.

Figure 5 presents the infrared spectra in the 1250 to 1400 cm⁻¹ region of the infrared spectrum of the ethylene/olefin copolymer. This region is characteristic of methylene (CH_2)

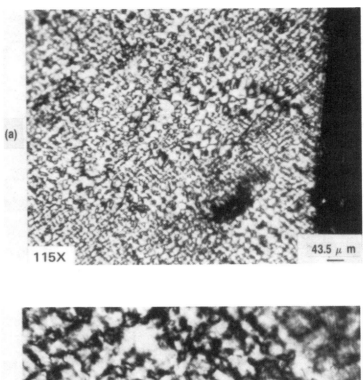

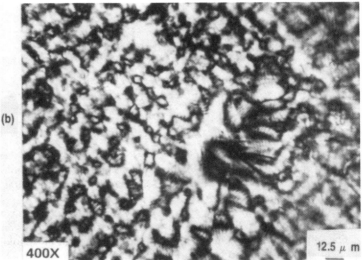

FIG. 3—*Polarized optical micrographs of bimodal morphology in ethylene/olefin copolymer,* (a) ×*115 magnification and* (b) ×*400 magnification, showing large spherulite region with dimensions of approximately 50 by 63 µm.*

wagging vibrations and vibrations of the methyl end groups of the side chain in the amorphous phase of the polymer.

Several regions containing large or small spherulites were sampled to obtain an accurate representation of the spectra from each phase. The results are representative of the trend observed in each of the spectra. The 15-µm-thick specimen required to observe the morphological features, which have been reported in the literature for similar types of polymers

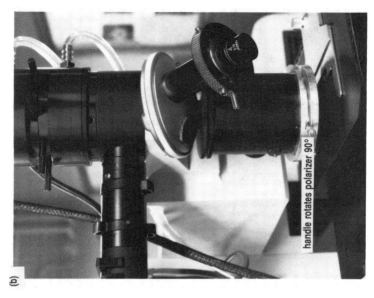

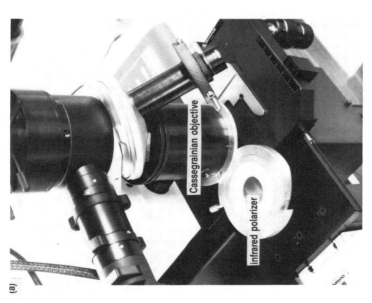

FIG. 4—*Photographs of the infrared polarizer attachment for the Cassegrainian objective in (a) configuration for viewing the specimen with visible light and showing the infrared polarizer and (b) configuration for recording infrared polarization data.*

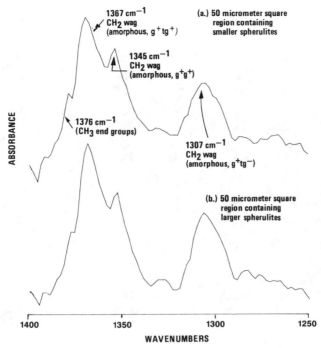

FIG. 5—*Infrared microtransmittance spectra in the 1400 to 1250 cm⁻¹ CH₂ wagging region for* (a) *50 by 50 μm region containing the smaller spherulites and* (b) *50 by 50 μm region containing the larger spherulites.* (*Collection conditions for the two spectra: 4 cm⁻¹ resolution, 2048 scans, post-specimen polarizer, and after subtracting water vapor.*)

or polymer blends, [10,11] resulted in infrared absorptions weak in the 1250 to 1400 cm⁻¹ region. Thus, this region of the spectrum was scale-expanded and trace amounts of water vapor were subtracted from the spectra.

Comparison of the two spectra show that the 1376 cm⁻¹ band due to the (CH₃) end groups is more concentrated in the region with the smaller spherulites. Also, the absorption band at 1345 cm⁻¹, CH₂ wagging vibration (g^+g^+ conformation), was more intense in the region with the smaller spherulites. These statements are made by establishing the 1367 cm⁻¹ band as the reference band. The greater concentration of the 1376 cm⁻¹ band in the spectra obtained from the smaller spherulites indicate that the branching is higher in this phase of the bimodal morphology. This would explain the smaller spherulite size being restricted from growing into larger spherulites because of the higher degree of branching. The cause of the larger absorption of the 1345 cm⁻¹ band in the smaller spherulite clusters is not clear. However, it is not the intention of this paper to discuss this in detail but to show how the technique can be used to obtain molecular information on various phases, domains, etc. of polymeric materials. Work is continuing in application of the technique to the study of polymer morphology.

This example has demonstrated that infrared microspectroscopy is very valuable for providing molecular information on specific domains, phases, etc. present in a polymer's morphology. This technique will open new areas of research in the field of polymer science and provide useful data explaining in detail the molecular origin of morphology in polymers (for example, copolymer domains, blends). This is true, of course, within the limits of the effective spatial resolution of the technique.

Multilayer Polymer Structures

A growing application of the use of polymeric materials is in the combination of several polymers to form multilayer structures or laminates that can be used, for example, as food packaging containers. The structures can be complex ranging from two layers to ten layers or higher. The layers can be of a variety of thicknesses depending on the function of the layer. For example, an adhesive polymer layer to hold two adjacent layers together may only be 3 to 10 μm in thickness. Barrier layers to prevent diffusion of oxygen can vary in thickness also from 5 to 25 μm or larger. Layers for structural strength vary considerably depending on the polymer and application but may be as thick as several hundred micrometres.

Infrared microspectroscopy is a valuable tool for studying the layers after a cross section of the material of an appropriate infrared path thickness has been prepared using microtoming techniques. The information can be used for qualitative identification of the layers or for understanding of the adhesion mechanism between two adjacent layers. In a previous paper the use of the technique to study a seven-layer polymer structure and the details of this study can be found [7]. However, it should be noted that with the technique, the optical microscope allows specific layers to be masked and infrared spectra recorded on layers as thin as 10 to 15 μm.

As with any technique, there are drawbacks. This will be demonstrated with an example. Figure 6 shows the optical micrograph of a cross section of a multilayer structure. The micrograph indicates the presence of three layers. The middle layer is an adhesive layer approximately 5 μm in thickness and was identified to be a polyurethane material. The

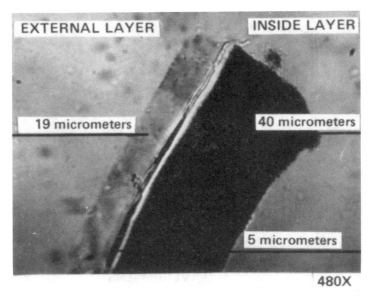

FIG. 6—*Optical micrograph of a cross section of a multilayer polymer structure used in food packaging applications (×480 magnification).*

laminate was studied using both ATR techniques of the surfaces of the film (25 by 10 mm specimen of film) and microtransmittance of a cross section of the film. Figure 7 shows the infrared spectra recorded of the external layer of the film. The microtransmittance spectrum (Fig. 7b) shows the 19-μm layer to be composed of cellophane. (This was also confirmed by standard transmittance spectra recorded on a film obtained of the external layer by solvent delamination.) The lower-frequency region of the spectrum does not show absorption

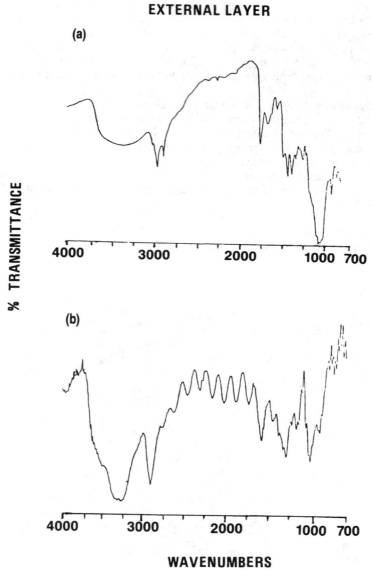

FIG. 7—*Infrared spectra between 4000 and 700 cm⁻¹ of the external layer for the cross section shown in Fig. 6. (a) ATR spectrum (4 cm⁻¹ resolution, 256 scans), (b) microtransmittance spectrum (4 cm⁻¹ resolution, 16 scans, 10 by 200 μm aperture).*

INSIDE LAYER

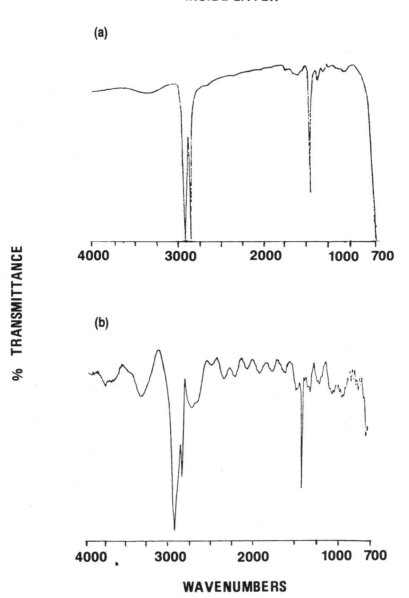

FIG. 8—*Infrared spectra between 4000 and 700 cm^{-1} of the inside layer for the cross section shown in Fig. 6. (a) ATR spectrum (4 cm^{-1} resolution, 256 scans), (b) microtransmittance spectrum (4 cm^{-1} resolution, 16 scans, 40 by 200 μm aperture).*

band intensities typically characteristic of cellophane (that is, the 1070 cm^{-1} band is more intense than shown in the spectrum). It is believed in this case that the 10-μm aperture used to record the spectrum resulted in scattering of the radiation at these lower frequencies. This resulted in distorted intensities. The ATR spectrum shows the surface features (2 to 10 μm penetration depth) to be indicative of cellophane but other absorption bands are also observed in the spectrum. These bands are due to a plasticizer blended with the material (a latex) used as the barrier layer for the film. The optical micrograph does not show this thin surface layer, and thus it was not considered to be present when recording the microtransmittance spectrum. This shows that the optical micrograph does not always identify the number of layers present in an unknown multilayer structure. Infrared spectroscopy can be used to view the specimen. As shown, the microtransmittance and ATR techniques are complementary in the information they provide. Figure 8 shows the ATR and microtransmittance spectra obtained for the inside layer of the polymer, which is identified by both techniques to be polyethylene.

The limit of the technique in obtaining spectra on specific layers is that layers thinner than about 10 to 15 μm cannot be obtained readily and "pure." In our laboratory, methods are being pursued to increase the effective spatial resolution of the technique.

Example of Infrared Reflectance Microspectroscopy

The examples presented thus far have used the transmittance capabilities of the technique. However, the reflectance capabilities can be valuable for studying surface related problems of polymer materials. Previously reported was the use of reflectance spectroscopy to study surface imperfections on the painted surface of a polyurethane [7].

Figure 9 shows the optical micrograph of a streak in a film of a blend of ethylene/acrylic acid (EAA) and ethylene/methacrylate (EMA) copolymers that is used to coat the surface of some aluminum foil (the film also contains titanium dioxide). The reflectance capabilities

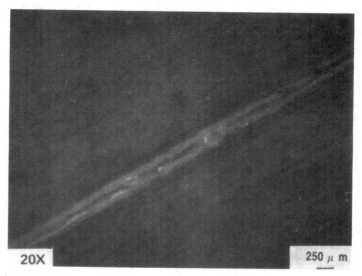

FIG. 9—*Optical micrograph of a streak in a film coating on aluminum foil made by blending ethylene/acrylic acid (EAA) and ethylene/methacrylic (EMA) copolymers (×20 magnification).*

were used to determine the composition of the streak in the film. Since the film is on aluminum foil, the spectra were obtained as reflectance/absorption spectra because the aluminum foil functions as a mirror. Figure 10 shows the reflectance/absorption spectra obtained for the streaked region of the film and bulk film sample using a 200 by 200 μm aperture. The spectra could have been recorded on areas as small as 10 to 20 μm², but because of the size of the streak a more representative sampling of this area was obtained from a 200 by 200 μm area. The spectra show that the EMA copolymer is in higher concentration in the streaked region than in the bulk film. This is observed by comparing the carbonyl stretching absorption bands for the EAA and EMA and the intensity of the EMA band at 1162 cm⁻¹. This was confirmed several times by recording spectra at various locations along the streaked region of the film. Because the streak contains more EMA than EAA, the processing of the film was influenced such that streaked regions (for which the film is thicker in the region) resulted.

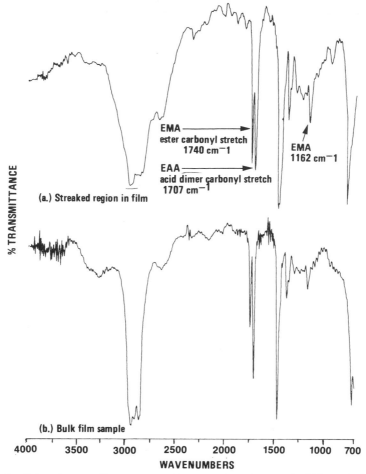

FIG. 10—*Infrared microreflectance spectra between 4000 and 700 cm⁻¹ of* (a) *streaked region in blend of EAA and EMA copolymer film on aluminum foil and* (b) *bulk film sample. (Collection conditions for the two spectra: 8 cm⁻¹ resolution, 256 scans, 200 by 200 μm aperture).*

Conclusions

Infrared microspectroscopy has been demonstrated, using several examples, to be a versatile and valuable technique for studying various aspects of polymeric materials. The technique can be used to study: (1) single particles, (2) gels, (3) laminates or multilayer structures, (4) single fibers, (5) coatings, (6) microscopic surface heterogeneities, (7) heterogeneous materials (for example, morphology), etc. The examples presented highlight the advantages of the technique over "standard" microsampling techniques—reduction in specimen preparation time and the specificity with which infrared spectra can be recorded.

The capabilities of the analytical tool for investigation of polymeric materials or other applications of the technique have not been severely tested. As mentioned earlier, the technique will be most useful for studying the molecular structure that gives rise to various phases, domains, etc. in the morphology of polymeric materials. Many additional areas of scientific research will benefit from the ability to use an optical microscope to view specific regions of a specimen and subsequently record the infrared spectra.

Acknowledgments

Many thanks to G. P. Young for preparing the microtomed cross sections of the polymers and to those who provided the specimens.

References

[1] Dybroad, J. P., Logan, L. M., and Zinnow, K. P., *American Mineralogy*, Vol. 1, 1974, pp. 604–607.
[2] Ramsey, J. N. and Hausdorff, H. H., *Microbeam Analysis*, Vol. 16, 1981, pp. 91–95.
[3] Scott, R. N. and Ramsey, J. N., *Microbeam Analysis*, Vol. 17, 1982, pp. 239–242.
[4] Brenner, D. in *Proceedings*, Society of Photo-Optical Engineers/International Society of Optical Engineers Conference, Vol. 411, 1983, pp. 8–12.
[5] Krishnan, K., *Polymer Preprints*, Vol. 25, 1984, pp. 182–184.
[6] Herres, W. and Zackmann, G., *Fresinus Zeitiscrift Analytical Chemistry*, Vol. 319, 1984, pp. 701–705.
[7] Harthcock, M. A., Lentz, L. A., Davis, B. L., and Krishnan, K., *Applied Spectroscopy*, Vol. 40, 1986, pp. 210–214.
[8] Smith, A. L., *Applied Infrared Spectroscopy: Fundamentals, Techniques, and Analytical Problem Solving*, Wiley, New York, 1979, pp. 117–118.
[9] Heavens, O. S., *Optical Properties of Thin Solid Films*, Academic Press, New York, 1955, pp. 238–240.
[10] Teh, J. W., *Journal of Applied Polymer Science*, Vol. 28, 1983, pp. 605–618.
[11] Tan, V. and Kamal, M. R., *Journal of Applied Polymer Science*, Vol. 22, 1978, pp. 2341–2355.

Ellen V. Miseo[1] and Louise W. Guilmette[1]

Industrial Problem Solving by Microscopic Fourier Transform Infrared Spectrophotometry

REFERENCE: Miseo, E. V. and Guilmette, L. W., **"Industrial Problem Solving by Microscopic Fourier Transform Infrared Spectrophotometry,"** *The Design, Sample Handling, and Applications of Infrared Microscopes, ASTM STP 949,* P. B. Roush, Ed., American Society for Testing and Materials, Philadelphia, 1987, pp. 97–107.

ABSTRACT: This paper is divided into two separate parts. The first part of the paper describes the permanent mount for an infrared microscope. The original design called for the microscope to be put in the infrared sample compartment of a Digilab FTS-15 spectrometer. Our changes allow the microscope to be permanently mounted using the original external beam configuration of the instrument with changes in the base plate optics on the microscope. The second part describes four analytical applications of the microscope showing how it can be used to substantially reduce sample preparation and allow examination of very small specimens. These four applications include identifying a lubricant in a nylon block, identifying a microcontaminant, elucidating an ink formulation, and looking at a multilayer polymer film.

KEY WORDS: micro Fourier transform infrared spectrophotometry (FT-IR), contaminant identification, FT-IR techniques

Since the introduction of commercial Fourier transform infrared spectrophotometry (FT-IR) instruments, spectroscopists have been trying to examine smaller and smaller specimens. The early work in this area [1,2] relied on having the skills of a microscopist combined with that of the spectroscopist to allow analysis of specimens in the nanogram range. Since a specialized skill was required, the analysis was not practical for most spectroscopists. With the introduction of microscope sampling accessories for FT-IR [3], analysis of microspecimens has become more convenient and is more easily accomplished by spectroscopists alone.

This paper will briefly describe two separate tasks. The first is a discussion of a permanent mount for a microscope accessory in a commercial FT-IR. The second part of this paper will describe the analysis of a variety of specimens using microsampling FT-IR.

Permanent Microscope Mount

The FT-IR system on which we use our microscope accessory is a Digilab FTS-15. In that particular instrument, the microscope accessory is meant to be mounted in the sample compartment. With the microscope mounted, one cannot use the spectrometer sample compartment for any other applications unless the microscope is removed. The inconvenience of this situation led us to permanently mount the microscope in the external beam of the FT-IR. Figure 1 shows a photograph of the microscope permanently mounted.

---

[1] Senior consultant and research assistant, respectively, Arthur D. Little, Inc., Cambridge, MA 02140.

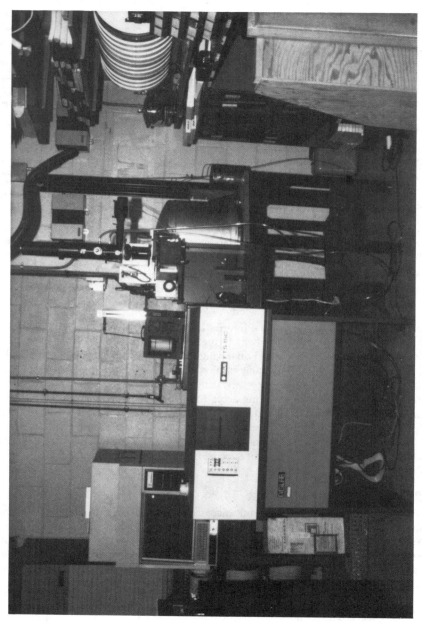

FIG. 1—*Permanently mounted microscope accessory.*

To achieve this mounting system we made use of some of the hardware, optics, and electronics from an old packed column gas chromatography/infrared (GC/IR) accessory. Our design involved changing the optics in the base of the microscope to accommodate both the beam entering from the left rather than the right and to bring the beam to a focus at the same point it occurs when mounted in the sample compartment.

A new base plate was constructed from 0.94-cm (⅜-in.) aluminum plate and three mirrors, a toroid, a flat, and a flat mirror at 45 deg to the horizontal were mounted on the base plate. Figure 2 shows a more detailed photograph of this arrangement. A box was constructed over the base plate to support the microscope at the proper height so that the beam would be in focus at its intended focus. This entire assembly with the microscope attached was then mounted on rails originally intended to support a GC/IR accessory. Another plate 0.63 cm (¼ in.) thick was bolted under the rails to give the assembly further stability.

The Digilab instrument was designed for use with a GC/IR accessory so that we were able to simply plug the mercury-cadmium-telluride (MCT) detector cable into the jack provided for a detector on the external beam. Since GC/IR applications require an MCT detector we had no problem making sure that the electronics were compatible.

Since the microscope is permanently mounted and not in the sample compartment, we now have the added flexibility of accessing the microscope with a simple switch; this results in use of the microscope for more applications.

Microscope Applications

Our applications of microscopic FT-IR are usually aimed at identifying materials or contaminants in commercial products. Four examples are described which are typical of this type of analysis. The four examples are a nylon block with a lubricant, an ink formulation, a microcontaminant, and a multilayer film. Except for the multilayer film, none of these

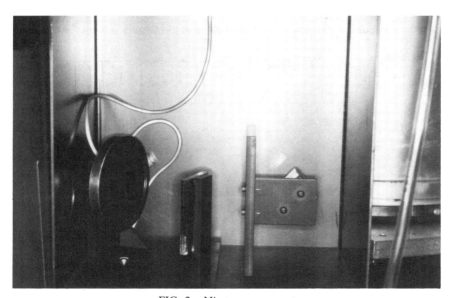

FIG. 2—*Mirror arrangement.*

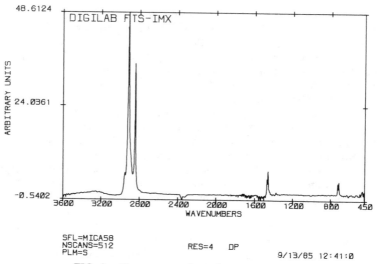

FIG. 3—*Clear area at edge indicating lubricant.*

applications required high spatial resolution, but all show the utility of the tool for quickly and easily solving the problems.

Lubricant in Formed Polyamide Block

For this analysis we were faced with a nylon block impregnated with a lubricant. We were interested in whether the lubricant material was a stearamide or a microcrystalline wax. The initial infrared (IR) spectrum of the material seemed to indicate only a polyamide indicating that the lubricant was present at a very low level.

The block was Soxhlet extracted using methylene chloride as a solvent, and a spectrum

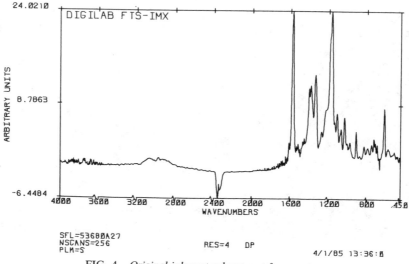

FIG. 4—*Original ink spot solvent cast from water.*

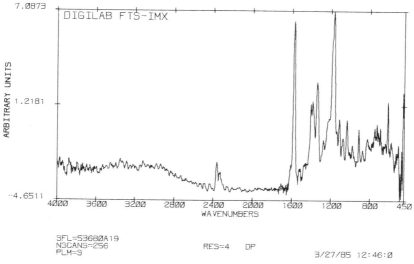

FIG. 5—*Acid blue 9.*

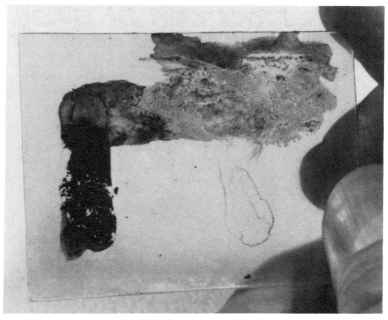

FIG. 6—*Separate experiment.*

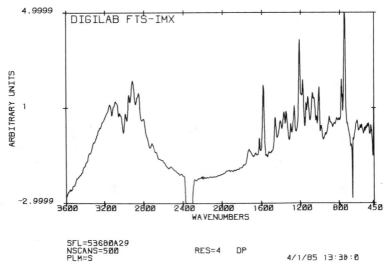

FIG. 7—*Second wash with methylene chloride shows mostly benzotriazole.*

of the extractables was run. The extract was applied to a potassium bromide (KBr) plate, and the solvent allowed to evaporate. As the plate dried it was obvious that two materials were separating on the KBr plate. An IR spectrum of the bulk material on the plate was ambiguous as to whether we were dealing with a stearamide or a wax since there were bands at 1650, 1550, and 3500 cm^{-1}. By using the microscope accessory we were able to examine the spectra of different areas of the specimen. In the areas that appeared slightly cloudy, we obtained an IR spectrum, shown in Fig. 3, indicating a microcrystalline wax type material.

In this particular application, we took advantage of an effect that is usually a drawback in evaporating materials from solvents. The microscopic accessory allowed us to easily

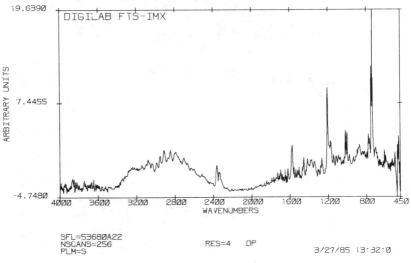

FIG. 8—*Benzotriazole.*

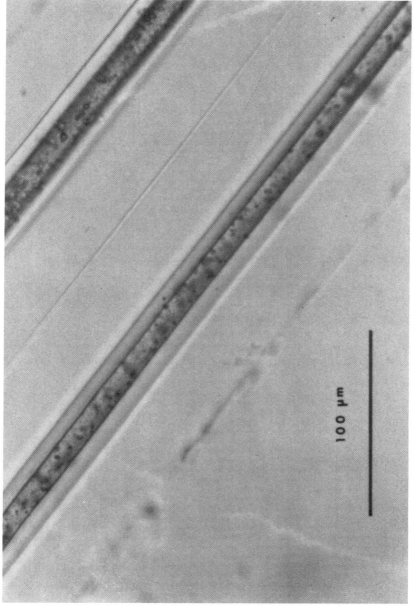

FIG. 9—*Photomicrograph of multilayer laminate material.*

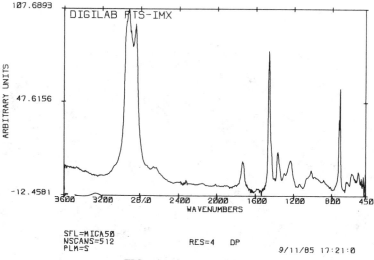

FIG. 10—*Laminate Layer 1.*

examine a variety of areas on the KBr plate to determine if we had two different materials and to differentiate the lubricating wax from the residual dissolved polyamide.

Additive in Ink

In many applications, we are asked to characterize a product to determine differences in formulations. We were given a commercial ink and asked to determine the components that were used to formulate it. The solvent system, a mixture of glycols, was relatively easy to identify, as was the major pigment, acid blue 9. Our difficulty came in trying to identify the

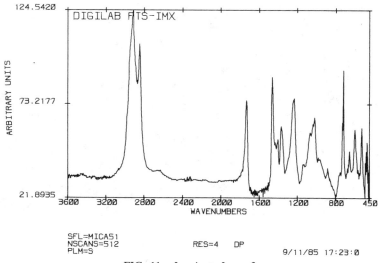

FIG. 11—*Laminate Layer 2.*

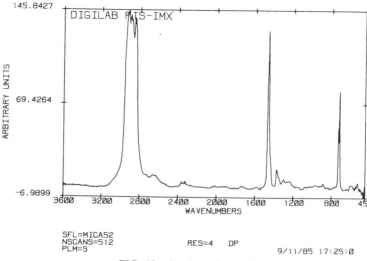

FIG. 12—*Laminate Layer 3.*

other component which gave the ink its physical properties and could not be accounted for by the dye, binder, and solvent system.

Figure 4 shows a spectrum of the original ink with the solvent and binder system removed. This sample was solvent cast from water. In Fig. 5, a spectrum of acid blue 9 is shown. The spectra are very similar, and it is apparent that the acid blue 9 is the major component. Our reference standards of acid blue 9 were not pure, and, unfortunately, we were not able to subtract the acid blue 9 to identify the other components.

At this point we tried to separate the materials with a liquid chromatography cleanup using silica gel and solvents with a range of polarities. In all the fractions we looked at from

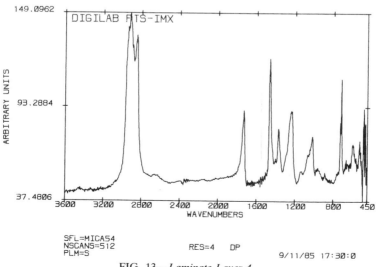

FIG. 13—*Laminate Layer 4.*

these separations, acid blue 9 was the dominant feature, and, although other features were visible, it was impossible to identify the material.

We then attempted an experiment to achieve some separation. As was noted in the previous example, materials with slightly different solubilities seem to migrate to different areas on a salt plate. Figure 6 shows a photograph of our experiment. We cast a spot of the ink from water onto a large silver chloride plate. The original spot is in the upper left corner of the plate. Then, using methanol, we washed the solubles to the right of the plate. Methylene chloride was then used to wash those solubles toward the bottom of the plate. A second methylene chloride wash was then done to form the faint spot in the lower left of the plate directly below the original spot.

Using the microscope we examined the various regions of the plate. Figure 7 shows the spectrum obtained from the last faint area. It is very different from that of acid blue 9 and was identified as benzotriazole. Comparison with Fig. 8 shows this. Subsequent work with compounding an ink using these components accounted for the physical properties of the ink, which was only duplicated with benzotriazole.

Microliter Volume of Contaminant

In the next application we were faced with a contaminant in an applicator used for medicinal purposes. We suspected a minor contaminant. Only 100 µL of an unknown concentration solution of the material was available. We took 10 µL of the solution and formed a small drop at the end of a syringe. The solvent was allowed to evaporate, and a minimum amount of the material was transferred to a small area on a KBr plate. The IR spectrum identified the materials as a simple mixture of tributyl phosphate, a common plasticizer and a polysiloxane commonly used as a mold release agent.

Multilayer Laminate

The final example was a multilayer laminate material. A photomicrograph is shown in Fig. 9. To prepare the specimen, one of the microscopists microtomed the specimen to give

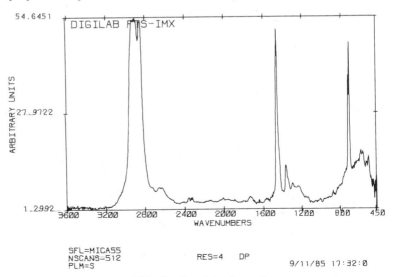

FIG. 14—*Laminate Layer 5.*

us a thin film across the face of the film. The slices were transferred to a KBr plate and examined. Figures 10 to 14 show all five layers of the material as seen in the photograph. The identifications of the layers are described next. Layer 1 was mostly a polyethylene with some contribution from polyvinyl acetate. Layers 2 and 4 show a spectrum of polyvinyl acetate with some polyethylene contribution. Layers 3 and 5 are clearly polyethylene.

As the spectra indicate, the spatial resolution to achieve spectral separation of each component was not achieved, but this could be easily remedied by a simple subtraction.

Conclusion

Although we have not pushed the microscope FT-IR accessory to its fullest capabilities of spatial resolution, these applications point out what is possible to achieve. In many of the examples this could have also been done by masking the specimen and using a traditional beam condenser, but sample preparation and data acquisition would have been much more difficult.

In many of these applications, we have also found it to be valuable to have the advice of trained microscopists. Many chemists, including those in the FT-IR community, need to develop similar skills in order to make better use of this new tool.

References

[1] Cournoyer, R., Shearer, J. C., and Anderson, D. H., *Analytical Chemistry,* Vol. 49, 1977, p. 2275.
[2] Lacey, M. E., *Proceedings of the Institute of Environmental Science,* 1983.
[3] Krishman, K. and Kuehl, D., Paper No. 238, presented at Federation of Analytical Chemistry and Spectroscopy Societies, 1983.

Author Index

Subject Index